THE REV

'This time we[...]
shall capture [...]
their brains up when we have removed them
from your world.'

'You wish to use the same children?' asked
Mr Salt.

'Quite right,' the Brain Sharpener informed him. 'Only by using the same children can I clear my name with my superiors.
In addition, I shall have great pleasure in
taking revenge on the children and their unfortunate teacher, Mr Browser, who is lucky
to have escaped our anger so far!'

Also in Beaver by Philip Curtis

Mr Browser Meets the Burrowers
Mr Browser and the Mini-Meteorites

THE REVENGE OF THE BRAIN SHARPENERS

Philip Curtis

Illustrated by Tony Ross

Beaver Books

A Beaver Book

Published by Arrow Books Limited
62-65 Chandos Place, London WC2N 4NW

An imprint of Century Hutchinson Limited

London Melbourne Sydney Auckland
Johannesburg and agencies throughout
the world

First published by Andersen Press Ltd 1982

Beaver edition 1987

Text © Philip Curtis 1982

Illustrations © Andersen Press Ltd 1982

This book is sold subject to the condition that it shall
not, by way of trade or otherwise, be lent, resold,
hired out, or otherwise circulated without the pub-
lisher's prior consent in any form of binding or cover
other than that in which it is published and without a
similar condition including this condition being
imposed on the subsequent purchaser

Made and printed in Great Britain by
Anchor Brendon Limited, Tiptree, Essex

ISBN 0 09 954090 8

Contents

1
The Space Commander's Ultimatum

Nothing annoys a Brain Sharpener more than to have his plans foiled by a creature of lesser intelligence. When the Outer Space Commander in charge of Expedition Earth discovered that Michael Fairlie had prevented Class 8's brains from being successfully sharpened, and that the pepper-pot craft was returning with only the unhappy Headmaster, Mr Salt, on board, he was as near to losing his temper as a Brain Sharpener can come.

When the craft arrived back at the Outer Space Station he lost no time in calling Mr Salt before him. The Headmaster found himself carried across the moving floor in the same way that Michael had been, and in a few seconds he was in front of the Commander's desk, standing there and wondering what was in store for him, just as children used to stand before him in his study at Chivvy Chase School.

'I was instructed,' began the Commander, speaking as correctly as a T.V. announcer – for the Brain Sharpeners had learned their English through listening to the radio and watching T.V. – 'to return to base with a group of children suitably sharpened up

to colonise a new planet. All I have here is one Headmaster. Our plans have gone wrong, and my superiors are demanding that I return. I am most displeased.'

'I'm very sorry,' said Mr Salt, though he really was feeling much more sorry for himself than for the wrinkled Brain Sharpener.

'You are of no use to me at all,' went on the Commander bluntly. 'You are only here because I didn't want you to spread stories about our craft. You are our prisoner, and I do not see how you can stay here for long. Why should we bother to keep a prisoner who requires special food and is a nuisance to us?'

8

'I don't know,' admitted Mr Salt miserably.

'It would be simpler to let you fly off into space,' went on the Commander.

'Oh no – don't do that, please! Spare me! Perhaps I can after all be of help to you?'

The Brain Sharpener put on an expression very much like a human sneer.

'How could you possibly help us?'

'Perhaps I could arrange to obtain some children for you so that you could sharpen up their brains – '

'I am allowing you to read my thoughts,' observed the Commander with a superior smile. 'I have decided to ask permission to make one more attempt to obtain these children as part of our experiment to develop our newest planet. Their brains were sharpening up admirably, until that foolish boy defied us. This time we shall make no mistakes. We shall capture the children first and sharpen their brains up when we have removed them from your world.'

'A good idea,' said Mr Salt.

'Thank you. And now you had better tell me how you can possibly be of assistance to us in the matter?'

'You wish to use the same children?'

'Quite right,' the Brain Sharpener informed him. 'Only by using the same children can I clear my name with my superiors. In addition, I shall have great pleasure in taking revenge on the children and their unfortunate teacher, Mr Browser, who is lucky to have escaped our anger so far!'

'I can perfectly well understand you,' observed the Headmaster, his knees quaking under the intense critical glare of the Commander. 'But it's difficult for me to see how I can help, though I'm prepared to do anything – '

'Then I will tell you. Clearly we do not wish to attract any more attention in the neighbourhood of Chivvy Chase School. To create more fogs there in the summer months would look very suspicious. Therefore the children must be taken a very long way from the school, where they can disappear without anyone seeing them go. Let it be thought that they have somehow been lost – killed, if necessary. Well – have you still no ideas? I can see that your brain will have to be sharpened. Look at me, and think!'

Desperately Mr Salt tried to think, with the relentless eyes of the Brain Sharpener seeming to bore into his head.

'I have it!' he said suddenly, his forehead wet with perspiration. 'I am very friendly with the Chairman of the Chivvy Chase School Parents' Association, Mr Portland-Smythe. He has a sister who lives in the north of Pakistan, a kind of missionary. I know he fancies taking a school trip out there, but everyone said it would be too far for the children. If I could persuade them, we could find some isolated spot where you could land in secret – '

'Excellent! Now you are letting me lead your brain. How could you most easily influence them? Can you return as Headmaster?'

'Yes, if they haven't appointed a new one yet. I expect Miss Toms is Acting Head for a while. I might have difficulty persuading them to have me back after my sudden absence – '

'Simple, Mr Salt! A nervous breakdown, you humans call it. After you've been on a sharp brain sharpening course up here with us, no one will be able to withstand your arguments.'

'Me – a brain sharpening course? I'm a Headmaster, I don't need a brain sharpening course!'

The Brain Sharpener looked at him with a curious expression, a mixture of pity and pitilessness.

'Your brain, my good sir,' he said, 'has only been sharp in certain ways. You are not even aware of how much you can be improved. Your course will start in a few hours' time by your watch – and in a week of Earth time we will have you in such a condition that no humans will be able to withstand the power of your brain!'

Mr Salt's eyes gleamed.

'Shall I be able to become an Inspector – even a Chief Inspector?' he wondered.

The Brain Sharpener thrust his ugly head forward, and Mr Salt retreated in fright.

'First,' declared the Commander, 'we want those children. We must have them within as short a time as possible after your return to Earth. You may go!'

The floor underneath Mr Salt turned suddenly round, the door opened and he was whipped away into solitary confinement, where he was kept for a whole week, between sessions of concentrated brain sharpening.

Spiky Jackson was first into the classroom on the opening day of the summer term. Not that he was an extra keen pupil – but he was bursting with news.

'I seen him, Mr Browser, I seen him!' he cried as he came straight to Mr Browser's desk. Mr Browser's heart sank because of Spiky's misuse of the verb 'to see', but he tried not to be too critical in the very first minute of the term.

'So. You have seen him, Simon. Say "I have seen him" before you tell me more.'

'I have seen him,' mouthed Spiky impatiently.

'And may I ask the name of the person you have seen? Possibly a pop star, or a T.V. actor, or a footballer – '

'No, no, Mr Browser. I've seen Mr Salt!'

Mr Browser paled slightly and sat down at

his desk.

'Mr Salt! Are you sure?'

Even as he was speaking, Mr Browser reflected that he had heard rumours about the possible return of Mr Salt to Chivvy Chase School, but he had dismissed them as unfounded. Unlike the other teachers, he knew that Mr Salt had been taken up in the Brain Sharpeners' spacecraft, and was likely to be a few million miles away, if he were still alive.

'Where did you see him, Simon? Maybe you were mistaken.'

'No, Mr Browser. You see, my mum gave me a model glider for my birthday. You shoot it up with an elastic band –'

'Come to it, boy, we haven't all day!'

'I am coming to it, Mr Browser. I was in the park on Saturday, and I shot my glider up and it sailed for a long distance, and came down right on the golf course, near one of the holes.'

'So?'

'Well, some important looking men were playing there, and a man had just hit the ball, and it was going straight for the hole, and my glider landed in front of the ball and stopped it. I ran to fetch the glider, but the man who had hit the ball reached it first and picked it up. I started to say I was sorry, because he was ever so angry – and then I saw it was Mr Salt!'

'Did he know you?'

'I think so. But he was so angry that he threw my glider away, and told me to clear off. He scared me, Mr Browser. Is he coming back to school?'

'I don't know,' said Mr Browser. 'Now go to your place, please, and settle down.'

'And, Mr Browser, he was playing golf with Martin's father!'

Martin Portland-Smythe was the son of the Chairman of the Chivvy Chase School Parents' Association.

There was much whispering as Spiky Jackson sat down, and Mr Browser noticed that Michael Fairlie was looking very pale and earnest.

14

'Please, Mr Browser,' called out Anna Cardwell, 'is it true that Mr Salt is coming back?'

'That is not for discussion,' said Mr Browser stuffily. 'Kindly take out your maths books, and don't call out again, Anna. We're back in school now.'

'You're making it up,' muttered Anna to Spiky, but Spiky shook his head.

'Honest I'm not. Could anyone mistake somebody else for Mr Salt?'

'I suppose not,' conceded Anna grudgingly.

'Working, please, Anna, not talking,' requested Mr Browser earnestly, and there was quiet in the classroom. Not everyone was working, however. Martin Portland-Smythe, a tall, serious, dark-haired boy sitting at the back of the class and several desks away from Spiky, was writing hard – but not in his maths book. He was scribbling on a scrap of paper he had brought out of his desk. As soon as Mr Browser took off his glasses to clean them, Martin folded the paper over several times, wrote SPIKY on it and thrust it into the hand of the boy in front of him. Martin nodded energetically towards Spiky, to make sure the message was passed on. The boy agreed, though, of course, a price had to be paid. The go-between unfolded the paper and read the message. Martin glared at him, and the boy shrugged his shoulders and passed on

15

the message to Anna's friend Thelma. After two more stages, the note reached Spiky, falling as if out of the sky on top of his desk, thrown there by someone sitting at the desk behind.

Spiky swiftly unfolded the paper and read the message. 'You did see Mr Salt. He spoke to my father on the 'phone last night. Martin P-S.' Spiky nodded to Martin. Just then the door opened and Miss Toms, the Acting Headmistress, walked in and made straight for Mr Browser's desk. If there was silence in a classroom when Miss Toms entered, she could still manage to make that silence purer and deeper. Class 8 was hushed as Miss Toms kind of hypnotised Mr Browser into turning his back to the class, as she had already done herself. Some words were muttered. According to Michael Fairlie, who was sitting near the front, Mr Browser mumbled, 'I heard a rumour' and 'back where we started' and Miss Toms said, 'Better the evil we know.'

Then she suddenly turned to the class. Pens and pencils rattled on the desks instantly.

'I have some news for you, children,' she said. 'I have just heard on the telephone that our former Headmaster, Mr Salt, has recovered from his illness and will be returning to the school on Monday morning next. I thought I would tell you at once, so that it doesn't come as a surprise next week.'

'Come as a shock, she means,' commented Anna when Miss Toms had gone. 'What's this about him being ill? I thought he'd disappeared. You know, taken off by the Br –'

'Anna!' Mr Browser spoke unusually sharply. Work was resumed – or it looked like it. In reality, as Mr Browser stalked up and down the room, pens were held in hands while minds were puzzling over the return of Mr Salt.

Mr Browser at last stopped walking and stood looking out of the window. He, too, was thinking about the return of the Headmaster, which seemed to be as mysterious as his earlier disappearance from the school field. Mr Browser had been trying to forget about the Brain Sharpeners, but now he wondered whether Mr Salt would be the same man after his encounter with them. For when Mr Salt had gone out on the school field and vanished, Mr Browser believed secretly that the Brain Sharpeners had taken him away. Would Mr Salt be under their influence, or had he really only suffered from a nervous breakdown and not been taken away in their pepperpot spacecraft at all? Mr Browser shivered, although it was a warm day, and he was pleased when the school bell rang.

'Old Salt's coming back!' yelled Spiky at the top of his voice as he ran out into the playground. 'Old Salt's coming back!'

17

'Back from where?' asked a boy from another class.

'Back from Outer Space, for all I care,' joked Spiky. 'All I know is, old Browser doesn't seem too keen about it.'

But games are more important than rumours, and as Spiky could find no one else particularly interested in Mr Salt's return, he joined the rest in playing a game of football.

2
Classroom Shocks

Spiky Jackson had been seated by Mr Browser next to Selwyn Jordan, in the hope that Selwyn would ignore Spiky's frequent interruptions and by working hard encourage Spiky to do a little work as well. Then Selwyn went down with an attack of chicken pox, and Spiky at once began angling for Michael Fairlie, who was sitting on his own near the front, to be allowed to sit next to him while Selwyn was absent.

'Please, Mr Browser, please! Only while Selwyn's away. And we will work hard, won't we, Mike!'

Michael nodded hard, and Mr Browser hesitated. 'Please, Mr Browser. We're both working on the same history topic – the Vikings.'

'Oh well, we'll give it a try,' said Mr Browser, letting kindness overcome his better judgement.

So, on a sunny morning in late spring, Spiky and Michael were supposed to be providing Mr Browser with some more work for marking – but this was one of the first warm days of the year, and their minds wandered. Others in the class were restless, and Mr Browser himself was taking longer than usual to mark each book, because he was wondering whether he should do some gardening that evening. The strength of the sun was increased by the large windows, which seemed designed for basking cats rather than working children.

'Bet you four marbles I can make old Browser tell us another tale about when he was out East,' whispered Michael.

'You're on – it's not hot enough,' replied Spiky. Michael's hand shot up high.

'Yes, Michael?' asked Mr Browser.

'Please, Mr Browser, it's very hot. Could we have the sunblinds down?'

Mr Browser took a long look at Michael. 'Your shirt's hanging out again, Michael,' he complained as he went across to lower the blinds. 'You're not an Indian, you know, even if it is warmer today. No sooner does the sun come out than you have to ask for the blinds to come down. Out in India they were really needed.'

Michael winked at Spiky. The four marbles were as good as his, he thought.

'I thought you were in Pakistan, not India, Mr Browser,' he said, looking innocent.

'They were one and the same, years ago,' explained Mr Browser.

'Was it really hot out there?' piped up Anna Cardwell, always quick to seize an opportunity to put off work. She was rewarded by a smile from

Michael and a frown from Spiky. Some pens were quietly put down on desks as the class realised that the bait was on the hook.

'Why, it was hotter than this in the cool season,' declared Mr Browser.

'Four marbles, please,' whispered Michael to Spiky. Nothing was going to stop Mr Browser now.

'In very hot weather you could fry an egg on the parade ground at midday. And when you drank a cup of tea you perspired so much that your prickly heat stopped itching for a while –'

'Please, Mr Browser, when you were on the North-West Frontier did you meet any tribesmen?'

Mr Browser gave Michael an odd look. 'Of course I met tribesmen, Michael. I lived among Pathans near the border of Afghanistan.'

'Afghanistan! That's the place the Russians went into. Did you kill any Pathans?'

The question came from the round-faced, fresh complexioned Anna Cardwell, whose eyes were sparkling in spite of her innocent expression.

'No, Anna, not all the Pathans were hostile. Why, one of my best bearers was a Pathan called Iqbal Khan.'

'Bearer, Mr Browser? Did he carry you around?'

'No, he didn't. Bearer meant servant. Iqbal was a very faithful servant. He was most upset when I had to leave for home. Mind, he always had to be given

21

orders – would never do anything of his own accord. Did I tell you how he once nearly set the signal office on fire?'

The class kept tactfully silent, and Mr Browser retold the story of how Iqbal Khan was holding a newspaper in front of the fire in order to create a draught, and when it caught fire refused to put it down until Mr Browser had given him the order. Could it be true that Mr Browser didn't know he had told that story before?

This time, as soon as the story was concluded, the class was disturbed when Martin Portland-Smythe, who seldom had much to say, started to give out noises like a kettle coming to the boil. He appeared also to be trying to touch the ceiling with his hand.

'What is it, Martin?' asked Mr Browser.

'Please, Mr Browser, would you like to go back and see some of those tribesmen again?'

Mr Browser was silent at first – taken aback because Martin wasn't usually cheeky – and somebody laughed.

'I haven't really thought about it, Martin. But it's much too far away for me to go back there, I'm afraid. You see, my expenses were paid, in those days –'

'But you could go back there this summer term, Mr Browser. I heard my father say so.'

There was more laughing, but Martin persisted.

'It's possible some of us may be going with you to Pakistan on a visit.'

'Indeed,' said Mr Browser, annoyed. 'That's the first I've heard of it. I'm going to the Isle of Wight sometime this summer, and for the rest of it I shall be in my garden. Now you'd all better get down to work. We have wasted enough time.'

Michael and Spiky made faces at Martin, annoyed because Martin had disturbed Mr Browser's memories. Anna jabbed him spitefully with her pencil point. Mr Browser walked thoughtfully up and down between the desks, looking to see that everyone was working, and at the same time pon-

dering over Martin's suggestion. He would have liked to dismiss it as a joke, but Martin's father was the Chairman of the Parents' Association, so Martin could just possibly have heard something. Probably he had it all wrong, he decided, and was about to return to his marking when the Headmaster, Mr Salt, came into the room. Mr Salt had now been back at school for a fortnight, and looked even more serious than before his absence. He had lines on his forehead and hollows in his cheeks, and his tall frame looked ready to bend in any direction the wind blew. He noted that all the pupils were busy, then addressed Mr Browser.

'All working hard, I see. Good class, Mr Browser. I'd like to see you at playtime, if I may. Mr Portland-Smythe has come up with an idea which will interest you.'

'I'll be there, Mr Salt,' said Mr Browser, and you could have heard a pin drop in the classroom as the Headmaster left the room.

'Please, Mr Browser, did Mr Salt come about our visit to Pakistan?' called out Spiky cheerfully when the door had closed behind Mr Salt.

'Get on with your work!' growled Mr Browser and not a word was spoken until the bell for playtime rang.

In the playground Martin was at once surrounded by a crowd of his classmates.

'Is it true about Pakistan, or were you only joking?'

'Perhaps your dad was kidding,' suggested the serious Selwyn.

'I don't think so,' said Martin, who was now regretting having spoken. 'You'd better wait and see, hadn't you!'

Mr Portland-Smythe was tall, like his son, but rather fat as well. He was sitting in Mr Salt's room telling the Headmaster how he intended to turn the school's Parents' Association into the best one in the land.

'We'll do things no other Parents' Association has ever done,' he declared. 'We'll organise visits and raise hundreds of pounds, and make Chivvy Chase School the envy of all the rest.'

'Good,' said Mr Salt – and there came a knock on the door.

'That'll be Browser now,' said Mr Salt eagerly. 'We can't put up with any nonsense from him, remember! Come in!'

Mr Portland-Smythe sprang to his feet and gripped Mr Browser's hand so that it hurt.

'Mr Portland-Smythe has had an excellent idea for a school visit,' began Mr Salt with a satisfied smile.

'Well, really Mr Salt started it all,' said the

Chairman, but Mr Salt shook his head modestly. 'I understand,' went on Mr Portland-Smythe, 'that you often relate stories about your time on the North-West Frontier, not far from Afghanistan, Mr Browser.'

'Perhaps now and again,' admitted Mr Browser warily.

'Good! It so happens that I am a man with connections, and this school is going to make history. Not for us local visits to the coast or the hills. Chivvy Chase School will be the first junior school to make a school journey to Pakistan. I have a sister who runs a Mission Home in the hills near Rawalpindi, and a pilot friend who will help us fix

26

up a chartered flight out there. So you will be able to take a number of your class on a visit to your old stamping ground, Mr Browser. You know a great deal about the area, and you'll make an excellent leader. Not many schools will have managed a school visit out East, will they now?'

Mr Salt nodded agreement.

'When do you intend to go?' asked Mr Browser.

'At Whitsun,' replied Mr Salt eagerly. 'I shall be going too,' he added, staring hard at Mr Browser.

'But – I was going away for a few days with my wife to the seaside – '

The Headmaster looked out of the window with a pained expression on his face, and Mr Portland-Smythe pretended that he hadn't heard.

'I – I'll think it over,' said Mr Browser.

'Good man; I knew you wouldn't let those children down!'

'Of course he'll come,' said Mr Salt, turning round to face Mr Browser suddenly. 'It's the chance of a lifetime. Nobody in his right senses would refuse!'

Mr Browser found his way to the door, and when he'd left Mr Portland-Smythe seemed uneasy.

'Are you sure he's the right man?' he asked. 'A bit of a dreamer at times, what with his music and his poetry.'

'Don't worry,' said Mr Salt. 'We'll take Miss

Toms with us, to look after the girls. She'll keep everyone in order.'

'Excellent,' said the Chairman. 'I'll start making the arrangements straight away.'

When he was left alone, the Headmaster rubbed his hands together and smiled to himself triumphantly.

'Quick work!' he muttered. 'With the Brain Sharpeners behind me nothing will stop me. I'll be in charge of all schools on their new planet before I'm finished!'

Class 8 waited quietly for the return of Mr Browser after playtime.

'Silent reading!' demanded that gentleman as soon as he came into the room. Silent reading at such a time was torture. Anna was the first to weaken.

'Please, Mr Browser, are you taking us to Pakistan?'

'Silence!' thundered Mr Browser, taking the class by surprise, for he seldom thundered. 'If you don't work hard, Anna, you won't be coming with me. I shall only be taking well behaved, hard-working children with me!'

'It must be true!' whispered Spiky, and Martin Portland-Smythe allowed himself a slight smile.

The class was stunned into silence for the rest of

the morning, but although they looked as though they were working, most of them were, like Spiky, trying to remember all the strange stories Mr Browser had told them about the North-West Frontier.

As for Mr Browser, he was trying to decide why he was so much against returning to his old haunts. He came to the conclusion that it was because he didn't much like the glint in Mr Salt's eyes when the Headmaster had informed him that he would be coming too.

3
Crash Landing

On the first day of the Whitsun holiday Mr Browser led a party of Chivvy Chase boys and girls out on the tarmac of the airport to their waiting plane. Miss Toms was following the children like a watchful sheepdog, and behind her came the Headmaster, Mr Portland-Smythe and his very nervous little wife.

'Anna Cardwell – stop dodging out of line!' threatened Miss Toms. 'There's still time to send you back home!'

'Do you think the pilot will let me have a go at flying the plane?' was Anna's excited response. 'They say it's very easy, once it's up in the air.'

Miss Toms didn't deign to answer this question and Anna turned her attention to another subject.

'Do you think Miss Toms will be as strict on holiday as she is in school?' she whispered to her partner, Thelma.

'At least she'll keep the boys in order,' replied Thelma.

'I'm sure I've forgotten my toothbrush,' called out Michael.

'You can't go back now,' Spiky told him. 'You'

have to clean your teeth with the bark of a tree, like Mr Browser told us some Indians do.'

They entered the plane and took their seats. Some parents were waving frantically to them, but they were all too busy settling down to notice them. Instructions were given, seatbelts were fastened, and the engines began to roar. Miss Toms calmly slipped some cottonwool into each ear, then sat back, expressionless, her dark, straight hair tied by a ribbon at the neck. She was a lady who was determined that no situation and no person – especially no child – should ever get the better of her.

'Mr Browser looks uncomfortable,' said Thelma. 'Do you think it's because he's going East again, or because he doesn't like flying?'

Mr Browser was nervously cleaning his glasses.

'Perhaps it's because he's sitting next to Miss Toms,' suggested Anna.

The noise of the engines took over completely as they climbed to gain height, and in a few seconds they were hundreds of feet up in the air. Spiky looked out of the window, and soon they were flying so high that he could hardly sense that they were moving.

The plane had been chartered to Mr Browser's party and to some other passengers who were due to leave at a stop in the Middle East, after which the Chivvy Chase party had the plane to themselves.

Occasionally the pilot made announcements to tell them about the area over which they were flying.

'We are now crossing the Arabian Sea,' he told them. 'We shall be arriving at Karachi Airport on schedule.'

'I sailed across this sea,' said Mr Browser enthusiastically. 'You could see flying fish gliding over the water, and at night lightning played for hours on the horizon.'

'There's lightning on the horizon now,' said Spiky, 'and it's beginning to look dark over there.'

At that moment the air hostess was called forward by the pilot. Then Mrs Portland-Smythe, who appeared throughout the flight to be expecting the plane to fall into the sea, sat up anxiously as her husband was called forward too. After a while he came back and spoke earnestly with Mr Salt, and then to Mr Browser and Miss Toms.

'It appears,' Michael heard him say, 'that there is a severe electrical storm over Karachi. We have been redirected to Rawalpindi – which is in fact better for us, as it is nearer to my sister's place and we shall be saved a long train journey.'

'Rawalpindi!' exclaimed Mr Browser. 'I was there during the war. A fine city, and not far from the Murree Hills.'

'That's where my sister's place is,' said Mr Portland-Smythe – though everyone knew this already.

because of the lessons they had been given before the journey started.

'Oh dear, I do hope we avoid the storm,' said little Mrs Portland-Smythe. 'I don't like storms when I'm on the ground, let alone up in the air.'

'Don't worry, please,' said Mr Salt confidently. 'I'm sure the pilot will avoid any danger.'

After a while Anna Cardwell pointed at something outside her window.

'What's that?' she demanded. 'Surely it's not fog!'

'They don't have fogs out here!' stated Selwyn.

'Looks like a cloud, down low,' said Michael.

'It is a kind of cloud,' declared Mr Browser. 'A cloud of dust. I remember how we used to shut all the doors and try to keep the dust out, and still it crept into our beds and into our tea –'

'He's off again,' muttered Spiky.

'I hope the plane is dust proof,' said Miss Toms. 'If there's one thing I can't stand, it's dust.'

The engines snorted and there was a slight bump as the plane changed course.

'There are lots more clouds in the background,' observed Anna. 'The sky's turning dark because of them.'

'The sun's going down,' Mr Browser explained. 'Twilight is very short out here. You can watch the sun going down.'

'It's not the sun that's moving!' protested the

scientifically minded Selwyn Jordan, but no one took any notice of him – they were too interested in watching to bother with scientific facts.

Their first eastern sunset was made more spectacular by the storm clouds on which the rays of the dying sun played. But Mr Browser had focused his attention on something else.

'There they are!' he announced. 'The first foot hills of the old North-West Frontier. Just as they used to look!'

'What did he expect?' commented Anna. 'Did he think the tribesmen had cut off the tops of the hills?'

The hills showed up like a series of uneven folds bare and lifeless. Spiky and Michael gave them a glance, then returned to admire the sunset. Suddenly it was dusk, and equally suddenly, after the last tiny arc of the sun had vanished, the dusk became darkness.

'Excuse me, Miss,' Mr Portland-Smythe asked the air hostess, 'but shouldn't we be in Rawalpindi soon?'

'We are trying to make contact, sir, but we are having to make diversions because of storms. Electrical storms can make communication difficult out here, and these seem to be particularly strong. We just have to be patient.'

'Indeed, I recall that communication between Karachi and Rawalpindi was often difficult,' M

Browser was saying. 'Partly because of the hills, but also because of atmospheric conditions. Dust storms don't help. And sometimes the tribesmen stole bits of telegraph wires –'

'He's at it again,' said Michael, but his companion Spiky paid no attention; Michael saw that he was staring hard at Mr Salt. The Headmaster was gripping the arms of his seat hard and gazing anxiously out into the night.

'Old Salt looks scared,' whispered Michael.

'I think it's the lightning,' said Spiky. 'Whenever there's a flash, he goes all tense, as if he expects something to happen.'

'Of course,' Mr Browser was bumbling on, 'that was in the days of old-fashioned Army transmitters. No doubt modern sets can soon overcome such difficulties.'

The passengers looked doubtfully out into the blackness. Only the tops of the hills were now visible, and the black clouds were mingled with the darkness of the night sky. A loud bang from the front of the plane made the passengers jump in their seats.

'An explosion!' cried Mrs Portland-Smythe. 'We're being hi-jacked!'

'We've been hi-jacked!' shouted Anna, sounding more excited than frightened.

'Don't be absurd, child!' said Miss Toms angrily,

and although she was speaking to Anna you could tell that she included Mrs Portland-Smythe in the telling off. 'Keep calm, children. Everything is all right. There's no one on the plane to hi-jack us. It was probably just an engine back-firing.'

'An engine back-firing!' whispered Selwyn. 'We're not on a motorbike!'

'Miss Toms is quite right,' said Mr Salt, standing up. 'There's no need to worry at all. I think perhaps we'd better draw the blinds down now, Miss – '

So the air hostess went round assisting the passengers to block out the view of a magnificent electrical storm through which the plane was passing.

'We're in the middle of it!' whispered Spiky. 'There's lightning all around us!'

'Spooky, I call it,' was Michael's verdict. 'I hope we move away from it quickly.'

The air hostess was called to the front of the plane by the pilot.

'I'm sure the engines sound different,' insisted Mrs Portland-Smythe.

'Fasten your seatbelts, please,' announced the pilot over the intercom. 'We are passing through some bad weather.'

Most of Class 8 proved quicker at fastening their seatbelts than some of the adults – except for Michael, who succeeded in mixing up his belt with

his shirt, and had to be untangled by Spiky.

'She's right,' Spiky muttered when the belt was fixed. 'The engines do sound different.'

'The pilot wishes me to inform you that he has the plane under complete control,' said the air hostess. 'We have been slightly struck by lightning, and damage has been done to an engine. It would be better to make a landing straight away than to try and struggle on to Rawalpindi. The landing equipment is in perfect order. There are plenty of place where a safe landing can be made, though it may be a bumpy one.'

She inspected all their seatbelts, then returned to the pilot. She had made everything sound perfectly natural by her calm manner; landing in a strange country in the dark was an everyday event, according to her.

The passengers reacted differently. Mrs Portland-Smythe quivered with anxiety, and her husband was fully occupied in consoling and comforting her. Miss Toms was watching the children in her usual hawk-like manner, ready to pounce should anyone show signs of panic. Mr Browser began cleaning his glasses, a sign of discontent; he was not so sure there would be many safe landing places in the area. Mr Salt sat and stared at the roof of the plane with a satisfied smile on his face.

'Old Salt's enjoying it all now,' commented Spiky. 'Seems to be in a sort of dream.'

The plane lost height. The passengers had strange sensations in their stomachs as the pilot swooped upwards again, as though to avoid some obstacle. The girls kept their eyes on Miss Toms, while the boys stared ahead of them, wondering how the pilot could possibly know where a safe landing place lay.

'Not much grows here,' said Mr Browser cheerfully. 'There won't be many trees or bushes in the way.'

'No need to worry,' intoned Mr Salt. 'No need to worry at all!'

The plane dropped sharply again.

'Hold on tight!' ordered the air hostess. The plane was descending like a lift. They waited as if for hours, not just seconds. Then they bounced, and the seatbelts prevented their heads from hitting the roof. They bounced again – and again – but each time the bounce was a little smaller; then came a grinding sound and the plane shuddered to a halt.

'They've done it! They've done it!' said Mr Salt in tones of admiration.

'They? Who do you mean, Mr Salt?' asked Spiky.

'Mean – why, the pilot, of course – and the air hostess,' said Mr Salt, turning angrily towards Spiky. 'Who else could I mean?'

'Sorry, Mr Salt,' said Spiky. 'You said "they" and

I forgot about the air hostess.'

Mr Salt accepted the apology with a wave of the arm – but Spiky was convinced that his question had upset the Headmaster for a second or so.

'Everyone outside!' the air hostess ordered, and Mr Browser and Miss Toms set about organising the exit from the plane. Michael shivered and tucked in his shirt as they huddled together in the darkness.

'Please move well away from the plane and stay there until the pilot gives you further orders,' requested the air hostess, and the shivering party withdrew across stony ground some fifty metres from the plane. The air hostess returned to the plane, and the passengers could see torches shining as she and the pilot inspected it.

'They're checking against possible fire,' said Spiky.

Michael grabbed his friend's arm. 'What's Mr Salt looking for now?' he whispered.

The Headmaster was standing with his head thrown back, searching the sky without ceasing, swivelling his head from one side to the other.

'Oh, still scared of lightning, I suppose,' replied Spiky, who was not very interested in what the Headmaster was doing because he was growing rapidly colder. Five minutes later the pilot appeared.

'Sorry about the rough landing, all of you,' he said. 'I couldn't trust the engines any longer – something odd had happened to them. The electrical storm seems to have upset the whole system.'

'Quite likely, quite likely,' boomed out Mr Salt's voice.

'There appears to be no danger of fire,' went on the pilot, 'so we'll be able to return to the plane soon. I think I've landed Mr Browser back in his old hunting ground, North-West Frontier territory. I hope that when it grows light in the morning he'll be able to tell us whereabouts we are.'

Mr Browser shook his head. 'Judging by all these stones, we're in a valley on the dried up bed of a river,' he said. 'One river valley looks the same as another out here, I'm afraid.'

'We aren't in Afghanistan, are we?' asked Mrs Portland-Smythe in a trembly voice.

'No, madam, I'm pretty sure of that,' the pilot assured her. 'I don't think I circled so far away from Rawalpindi as that. But I should think we're in tribal territory.'

'Then I hope we've fallen in with the right sort of tribe,' observed Mr Browser. 'Some of them don't like strangers arriving without knocking at the door first, as you might say.'

'Oh dear, oh dear,' mumbled Mrs Portland-Smythe.

'Oh, there's no danger,' said Mr Browser, 'especially if we can return to the plane. We'll be safe enough in there.'

'I hope we can,' called out Anna. 'It's so cold out here.'

'Yes, Mr Browser,' said Spiky. 'You made a mistake when you talked to us about this part of the world. You couldn't fry an egg on the ground now – it would be more likely to freeze.'

'Just wait until morning,' retorted Mr Browser.

'Are there really dangerous tribesmen around here?' asked Anna.

'No, no,' said Mr Portland-Smythe quickly. 'I'm sure you decorated some of your yarns to make them sound exciting, didn't you, old chap?'

'Well – er – yes, I suppose so,' agreed Mr Browser.

'Of course he did!' declared Mr Portland-Smythe, as though challenging anyone to disagree with him. 'What's more important is that some of you are shivering. As soon as we can, we'll return to the plane and make ourselves as comfortable as possible for the rest of the night. I shall then help the pilot to get his transmitter working, so that we can have help sent here first thing in the morning.'

Soon the party was being conducted back to the plane, where blankets kept ready for an emergency were handed out. These they shared between them,

and settled down to make the best of things for the night. To Spiky it seemed like being at the bottom of a pitch black well, deprived of sight or hearing; from the outside no sound came.

'One good thing,' he said as he pulled the blanket over him, 'the neighbours are very quiet, so we shouldn't be disturbed.'

'Just see you don't disturb anybody yourself, Spiky!' Anna warned him.

'Try to have some sleep, all of you,' Miss Toms urged them. 'Good night, everyone.'

The aeroplane lay like a silent, prehistoric monster in the darkness. Inside it the passengers twisted and turned and found sleep difficult, as they lay

43

there wondering what was going to happen to them on the next day.

Mr Salt could not sleep at all; every so often he pulled back his window blind and looked out, as if expecting to see something more than the overall blackness.

Suddenly there came a frightening sound, something between a howl and a laugh, from away in the hills. Some heads popped up anxiously.

'Don't worry,' said Mr Browser. 'That was a hyena. I expect it's leading a pack of jackals in search of food. I've heard that sound many times.'

This was comforting, at first, and the passengers managed to fall into a fitful sleep; but not before some of them, like Spiky Jackson and Selwyn Jordan, had time to reflect that Mr Browser had told them about hyenas on several occasions, and if that part of his stories were true, then maybe the rest of them could be too – in spite of what Mr Portland-Smythe had said.

4
Tribal Welcome

Spiky and Michael, like most of the rest, dozed now and again, sometimes being wakened by each other's movements, sometimes because it was cold on the plane in spite of the blankets, and the seats were not designed for comfortable sleep. Now and again Spiky peered out into the darkness; in England, even when he had gone camping, there had usually been a friendly light twinkling somewhere in the distance, but here there was unrelieved blackness.

Once he awoke to hear the sound of quiet voices. Mr Browser was talking to the pilot.

'I calculate we're somewhere west of Rawalpindi,' the pilot was saying.

'That could place us in the territory of the Miralis, or possibly the Razirs,' said Mr Browser. 'There ought to be a road not many miles away. We used to send troops up to the barracks at Razmak in Waziristan on special days –'

'What sort of people are these Razirs and Miralis?' asked the pilot.

'A cheerful lot. Mind, they were always ready to ambush lorries or snipe at us. If they couldn't shoot at us, they'd shoot at each other. If a Razir killed a

Mirali, then it was the duty of the dead man's friends and family to kill a Razir in revenge. And so on. But they're also very friendly people. Friends are always given an excellent time. When I was out here for a while I had a servant called Iqbal – a Mirali. He was only a lad then, but he was most helpful, as I've told my class – '

'Yes, yes,' said the pilot. 'I'm sure you're right. But I'm glad I have my revolver with me, all the same.'

'What worries me more,' admitted Mr Browser, 'is that it could become devilish hot tomorrow. I don't know how the passengers are going to stand up to the heat.'

'Let's hope we establish communication soon,' said the pilot. 'You'd better get some sleep now.'

Spiky watched Mr Browser creep back to his seat. He wasn't much comforted by what he had heard, but weariness overcame him again, and he slept for another couple of hours. The next time he woke, Michael was tugging at his sleeve.

'Spiky! It's getting light. Have a look at this wilderness we've landed in!'

Spiky rubbed his eyes and blinked. Michael had pulled away the blind, and outside a grey light was turning the mystery of night into cold day. Spiky could see a stretch of stony, flat land, then a hill which rose gently until a steep slope led up to a ridge.

'Nothing but rocks and stones,' whispered Michael.

'What about the other side of the plane?'

'The same,' said Michael, after creeping across the gangway on an expedition of discovery. 'Hills all around, a few scruffy bushes and nothing else but stones.'

'It's a desert of stones!' observed Spiky. 'It could be a dried up river bed, as Mr Browser said –'

A slight sound as though something had fallen outside the plane cut Spiky short. Both boys listened intently, but heard nothing more. Then Michael pointed excitedly, and Spiky turned again to the window.

A man was walking steadily away from the plane, picking his way between the stones.

'It's Mr Salt!' whispered Michael. 'Whatever is he up to?'

'He's probably tired of being cramped up in the plane,' said Spiky. 'I'm a bit fed up, too. What about following him?'

Michael considered for a moment.

'We shouldn't really leave the plane –'

'I know we shouldn't. But we won't go far. Look – the sun's rays are appearing on top of the ridge. It'll be warmer up there. Come on – no one's going to stop us. They're all snoring.'

'Suppose Mr Salt sees us?'

'We won't let him. We'll hide behind rocks and bushes. Besides, he won't be able to say much, since he's left the plane secretly himself.'

Michael nodded, and they crept along to the door of the plane. The steps down to the ground had either been left in position all night, or Mr Salt had positioned them himself. The boys jumped lightly to the ground.

'What about wild animals?' asked Michael.

'Not many in the north, according to Mr Browser. Mostly camels.'

'We heard a hyena.'

'So what? Foxes come into back gardens in England at night.'

They looked ahead of them to see Mr Salt beginning the climb up to the ridge.

'I bet it's much warmer up there,' said Spiky, who was shivering. 'Let's go round another way, so that Salt can't see us. There are some bushes to the right of us – he'll never see us if we go that way. Maybe we'll see some houses on the other side of the ridge. Perhaps that's why he's gone up there.'

'Maybe,' agreed Michael.

'Race you to the top – but don't kick any stones about.' Michael accepted Spiky's challenge, and immediately they were off. For the next minute or two they were forced to look down at the ground ahead of them in order to pick their way success-fully between the stones and small boulders in their way. When they reached the bank of the dry river they stopped for breath before starting to climb.

'Where's Mr Salt?' asked Michael, and they gazed up to the top of the ridge, just in time to see the Headmaster disappearing down the other side of the hill.

'Let's go!' said Spiky. 'I want to see where he's off to!'

'Nowhere, probably,' said Michael. 'But it looks warm up there, so I'll race you to the top.'

They began scrambling up the hillside, but as often happens, the climb was longer and harder than it had at first appeared. They were still a hundred metres from the top when Spiky stopped for breath.

'We'll soon be out of the shadow,' panted Michael. 'It's shrinking down the hill towards us.'

'Look at the plane,' said Spiky. 'It's a wonder we made a safe landing!'

The plane was lying like a stranded whale on the river bed, surrounded by little stones and bigger boulders, which by good fortune it had avoided in its emergency landing.

'Perhaps we ought to hurry back!' said Michael. 'If they wake up and find us gone without permission, we'll be in trouble.'

'Trouble?' said Spiky. 'What worse trouble can we be in? Come on–we'll tell them the truth – we're following old Salt! Go back on your own if you don't dare to come.'

'Of course I dare!' declared Michael, and the two of them set off again with fresh determination.

'If I get there first, I'll call the ridge Spiky's Ridge,' challenged Spiky.

'Michael's Mount sounds better,' responded Michael – and the race was on.

Anna and Thelma were still sleeping, but their seats had become so uncomfortable that each of them began to claim extra space from the other, so that their arms and heads kept on tangling together. Thelma at last opened her eyes after receiving a sharp blow on the head from Anna's elbow.

Miss Toms was sleeping with her mouth open. Thelma looked politely away, and saw that the tops of the hills had bright sunshine on them. Anna turned awkwardly and nearly fell off her seat, wakening one or two more members of the party. Miss Toms stirred, woke up and closed her mouth instantly, looking around to see if anyone had observed her while she was asleep. She noticed at once that Mr Browser was not in his seat.

'Where's Mr Browser?' she demanded.

'I'm here,' came Mr Browser's voice, and he came back from the front of the plane. 'We've been trying to establish radio contact, but conditions seem unusually bad. Funny, because they always used to improve in the early morning. It's as though everything electrical has gone dead. Very odd. Of course, we're surrounded by hills – '

'Mr Browser!'

Miss Toms pointed to the empty seats of Spiky and Michael. 'Those boys – where are they?' she demanded. Mr Browser stared helplessly at the empty seats.

'Perhaps – ' he began, but couldn't think of what more to say, for he knew the boys were not up front.

'So you don't know where they are!' accused Miss Toms.

'No,' replied Mr Browser. 'Do you?'

'Someone has opened the exit door,' put in Mr Portland-Smythe, who had just woken up.

'Surely,' began Miss Toms threateningly, 'they haven't been allowed to go outside?'

'Mr Salt is missing, too,' said Mrs Portland-Smythe.

'Isn't he with the pilot?' asked Miss Toms.

'No,' said Mr Browser.

'They have gone out, Miss Toms!' burst out Anna Cardwell. 'I can see them climbing that hill over there!'

The blinds all went up as she pointed towards the nearest ridge.

'Confound them!' said the pilot, who had come to join the passengers. 'They must have slipped out while we were trying to make radio contact, Browser.'

'And I thought a watch was being kept!' grumbled Miss Toms. 'If only I'd stayed awake all night myself!'

'Come, Miss Toms, no harm has been done,' said the pilot. 'What do you think of the land, now that you can see it clearly, Mr Browser?'

'We're in a wadi,' said Mr Browser. 'That's a dried up river bed in a valley. There must be hundreds of wadis much like this one. It could be very near a place I stayed in once, but I couldn't be sure. The area could be absolutely deserted. We can't risk anything, though, so I'd better call them back at once.'

'Why wait, then,' observed Miss Toms, and he went to the door and shouted to the boys. After several calls Michael and Spiky stopped, turned round and waved. When Mr Browser signalled to them to return, they pointed to the top of the ridge, now only about twenty metres above them, and started climbing again.

'I'll tell them a thing or two when they come back!' threatened Miss Toms.

'I'll have to go and fetch them,' declared Mr Browser.

'I'll come with you,' volunteered Mr Portland-Smythe, and his wife clutched at his sleeve to stop him. Mr Browser was already away and had slipped to the ground.

There was a crack, and then a thud as something crashed against the side of the plane.

'Who's throwing rocks?' called out Anna.

'Stay where you are!' shouted Mr Browser to Mr Portland-Smythe, who had escaped from his wife and was at the doorway. 'That was a tribal bullet!'

Tak-dum! Another bullet crashed into the side of the plane as Mr Browser scrambled back into it

for cover.

'They're not very friendly,' said the pilot. 'I can'
see anyone firing at us.'

'They're experts at keeping under cover,' said M
Browser.

'Those poor boys,' said Miss Toms brusquely
'Are we going to leave them out there unprotected?

'What can we do?' said Mr Portland-Smythe. '
wish I'd never thought of this trip to Pakistan.'

'Why are they shooting?' cried his wife.

'Maybe they're only doing it for fun, or as
warning,' suggested Mr Browser, not very convin
cingly. 'They love to shoot at things, to kee
themselves in practice.'

'Whatever becomes of the boys, or of Mr Salt, wherever he may be, we can't risk anyone else going out at the moment,' decided the pilot. 'They're not in sight any more, and maybe they won't be spotted by the man firing at us.'

'Those disobedient boys!' complained Miss Toms.

'And why did Mr Salt go out?' asked Selwyn. 'Maybe the boys were only following him.'

'That could be,' admitted the pilot. 'I thought at first that Mr Salt was somewhere on the plane, but it does look as though he's left us too. All we can do is try to make contact with Rawalpindi and tell them what's going on. I'm afraid the boys and Mr Salt will have to take their chance for a while.'

'Those poor little boys!' sobbed Mrs Portland-Smythe.

'Oh, be quiet, woman!' declared Miss Toms – and Anna and Thelma knew that she had spoken like that because she was herself worried about Spiky and Michael.

Everyone stared out at the barren hills and the sinister ridge over which the boys had disappeared.

'I wish I'd never said a word about the North-West Frontier,' muttered Mr Browser.

'Those tribesmen will have to be taught a lesson!' Miss Toms declared. 'Firing at innocent people like that! I've never lost any children in any of the school parties I've been on before, and now there are two missing at once! Those tribesmen will have to suffer for it if any harm comes to them.'

'Yes, Miss Toms,' said Anna, and she couldn't help wondering what Miss Toms would do to the tribesmen if she ever did catch them. Now there was nothing to be done but to wait – and to hope.

5
Mr Salt's Rendezvous

Mr Salt tried to show surprise when the radio receiver on the crashed plane failed to bring in any signals, but in fact he knew very well that the Brain Sharpeners were putting into effect the first part of their plan. Now and again during the night he was tempted to go out into the dark to discover if one of their pepperpot shaped vehicles was already waiting to receive the children, but he feared he might lose himself, and decided to wait until a stronger message came to his brain from his masters from outer space.

Just before dawn he awoke with a strange buzzing sensation inside his head – and he knew the moment had come. He slipped unobserved out into the darkness, and the signals in his head told him which way to go. Just as a radio will receive stronger signals when it is placed in a certain position, so the buzzing in Mr Salt's head became stronger when he moved across the dry river bed in the direction of the ridge.

Once he fell over a large stone, and had to bite his lip in order to stop himself from calling out in pain as the stone grazed the skin off his shin. When he found he had to start climbing, the Headmaster began puffing and panting. The Brain Sharpeners had sharpened up his mind in the way they wanted, but they hadn't bothered to improve his physical fitness. He took a long time to reach the top of the ridge, and as he looked across on the other side he saw the first rays of the morning sun lighting the summits of the hills.   ·

Although he believed he had the protection of the Brain Sharpeners, Mr Salt became afraid as he gazed out at the bare, unfriendly countryside, which looked to him to be an ideal home for bandits and robbers. It was to be hoped that the Brain Sharpeners wouldn't leave him too long alone in this hostile territory! As the sun itself appeared, he saw smoke rising from a collection of greyish buildings down in the next valley. At first he was pleased to think that other people were about, but then his fears of robbers possessed him again, and he also was afraid lest he be discovered before he had achieved his meeting with his masters.

A sudden increase in the buzzing when he turned to his right directed his attention towards a hollow which was almost hidden from him by a fringe of low bushes round its edge. He was facing the one gap in the bushes which enabled him to see into the hollow.

'That's the place!' he muttered, as though someone had put the words into his mouth. He started to walk in the direction of the hollow, and the buzzing in his head grew ever stronger. When he reached the gap, he paused to look behind him.

What he saw made him dart swiftly for the cover of the bushes; a tribesman, with a rifle slung over one shoulder and a bandolier of ammunition hung around him, was striding quickly up a path from the houses to the ridge. Mr Salt's heart beat fast, so that he scarely noticed that the buzzing sound had died away. He had arrived at the place ordained for his rendezvous with his Brain Sharpener masters.

There was no sign of them yet, and Mr Salt became impatient and anxious. The sun's rays were

growing stronger, and were beating down on his unprotected head. Surely he hadn't made a mistake? Could the Brain Sharpeners have changed their minds and deserted him?

Tak-dum! Mr Salt jumped at the sound of a tribal bullet hitting its target. He guessed that the bullet had been fired by the lone tribesman he had seen on the path; but what had he been firing at? Could it have been the plane?

Another shot echoed round the hills. Mr Salt shivered. He dreaded having to go back to the plane under fire in order to fetch the children, even at the command of the Brain Sharpeners. He shifted his position uneasily, trying to gain the greatest amount of shade and shelter from the meagre cover of the bushes.

When the whirring sound began, mysterious though it was, Mr Salt welcomed it as a friendly sound. He had heard it once before, on the school field on the day when he had first met the Brain Sharpeners and been carried away by them. As the sound increased, dust from the hollow was stirred up and rose in a small cloud, so that anyone familiar with the area would at once have recognised the presence of one of those dust storms so common in Pakistan.

Mr Salt quickly took off his jacket and covered his head with it, trying to preserve a little dust-free air for breathing. The whirring sound died away, but dust was still in the air, and Mr Salt remained in a stork-like position, head near the ground, for a minute or so afterwards. When he looked out from the shelter of his jacket, he gasped in surprise in spite of the dust.

In the middle of the hollow a huge white pepperpot object was standing. It was much larger than the others he had seen; clearly it was for use as a transport carrier. As he stared at it a door began to open in the side of it, and the buzzing began once again in Mr Salt's head. Like a man in a trance, he stood up, put on his jacket and walked towards the pepperpot. Only when he had entered it did the buzzing cease. The door closed, and Mr Salt stared around at the bare sides of the pepperpot looking for some way of making contact with his masters. He need not have worried. The voice of the Commander of Expedition Earth suddenly boomed out above him.

'There is no time to waste,' it said. 'The humans in these parts are strange to us. One of them has fired on the transport vehicle with the children in it. We must collect the children before other attacks are made. You will go at once and bring the children here.'

'Yes,' said Mr Salt. 'But –'

'No buts!' declared the Commander. 'You will go

and fetch them! If this enterprise should fail, my reputation as Commander of Expedition Earth will be ruined. I shall be despatched to some minor planet and put in charge of a colony of Ancient Brain Sharpeners, or even made to retire! This mission must not fail! Go at once.'

'But – there's a man with a gun somewhere out there. Aren't you going to protect me?' asked Mr Salt.

'Protect you? We have sharpened your brain, and that must be your protection. You told us you would direct us to a lonely place where the children could be taken away without any fuss – and here we are. We do not use weapons, if that is what you expect. Our all-conquering method is the development and control of brains. This vehicle is simply designed to take our brain slaves from one place to another – if necessary, from one planet to another. Persuade the children here, and we can send out rays which will encourage them to obey blindly and enter the vehicle. It is for you to bring them in sight of us. Depart!'

The door opened swiftly, and Mr Salt stepped fearfully out; the door closed instantly behind him. As he advanced and climbed up the few metres to the rim of the hollow, he dreaded to hear the sound of another shot; but none came. He took shelter behind a bush and looked down at the plane, now glittering in the sunshine. He waited for five minutes, although he realised the Brain Sharpeners could be growing impatient. All seemed peaceful. How was he to persuade the children up the hill and into the hollow, within reach of the power of the Brain Sharpeners? In a flash the answer came – as if put into his head by the Brain Sharpeners themselves. He would persuade the children and the adults that there was shade and shelter from the heat in the hollow; the heat must be growing intense inside the plane. He would lead the children on, and tell the other adults that they could follow if they wished. If the Brain Sharpeners didn't want the other adults aboard, then no doubt they would find a way to reject them if they arrived on the scene too soon. Mr Salt's spirits rose, and he plucked up the courage to start walking down the hillside, confident still that the Brain Sharpeners would take care of him. There was no more shooting, and Mr Salt wondered why. He was inclined to believe the Brain Sharpeners had wider powers than they had suggested, and that he was under their protection. As he walked, the sun beat down upon him and soon his shirt was clinging to him and the perspiration was pouring down his nose. He began to wish he had thought of a more comfortable place in which to rendezvous with his masters.

Then he saw someone standing at the door of the

plane and waving, and he waved back and started to run down the hill, in spite of the heat and the danger of tripping over small rocks on the way.

The real reason why there was no more shooting was very different from that imagined by Mr Salt. Back in the plane, after some time had passed by without any repetition of the shooting, Mr Browser became more and more restive.

'We can't leave those two out there!' he declared. 'I must go out and try to find them. They could so easily become lost or even be captured if they are found wandering about in tribal territory.'

'I'll come with you,' said Mr Portland-Smythe at once, but the pilot objected.

'We can't have all the menfolk rushing off and leaving the women and children practically unprotected,' he said. 'I have a revolver, and there is a spare one for someone else, but that's the only defence we have.'

'No it isn't!' said Miss Toms, and Anna and Thelma opened their eyes wide as their Deputy Headmistress produced a neat little pistol from her handbag. The pilot opened his eyes wide, too.

'Is that loaded?' he asked.

'Of course it is,' said Miss Toms. 'My grandfather gave it to me, and I wasn't going to travel out East without bringing it with me, just in case.'

So that was the lesson Miss Toms intended to teach the tribesmen! Anna Cardwell stared at Miss Toms with a new admiration.

'Can you fire it, Miss?' she asked.

'Of course,' answered Miss Toms without looking at Anna. 'So we have three guns available. I think we can spare Mr Browser to go and look for his pupils.'

'But should he go alone?' persisted Mr Portland-Smythe, who was possessed by guilt for having brought the party into such a dangerous situation.

'Yes,' said Mr Browser, as if the matter were already decided. 'I know the country and the people, and I can speak a few words of Urdu, the common language out here. I must be the one to go.'

He didn't mention how long ago it was since he had been in the area, or that the tribesmen's real language was Pushtu.

'I think Mr Browser is quite right to go now,' said Miss Toms, as though she were giving him full marks for good behaviour. 'If we leave searching for them any longer, they're much more likely to lose themselves.'

'Better take the spare revolver with you,' suggested the pilot, but Mr Browser waved it away.

'I'll stand more chance without a weapon,' he said. 'I'll have to take a chance that we've landed in the territory of a friendly tribe.'

'But what about the shooting?' put in Mrs Portland-Smythe.

'Oh, probably that was just someone having a little practice,' replied Mr Browser. 'They'll fire at anything in these parts.'

Selwyn, Martin, Anna and the rest crowded to the windows as Mr Browser left the plane.

'Good luck!' cried Anna – and then they waited anxiously for the sound of a shot. None came. Mr Browser threaded his way between the stones and took to the hillside. He climbed slowly but steadily, as though used to the terrain.

Suddenly he stopped and sat down on the ground.

'Oh dear – is he feeling ill?' suggested Anna.

'Just having a rest, I expect,' said the pilot. 'He was probably thinner when he was out here before.'

'He's tying knots in his handkerchief,' announced Mr Portland-Smythe, who had brought some binoculars along with him.

'Whatever for?' asked Martin.

'I know,' explained Selwyn. 'He's going to put it on his head, to help to keep the sun off him.'

And Mr Browser did just that, then stood up and continued his climb. Ten minutes later he was at the top, and still no shot had been fired.

'Now he'll be able to see where they are,' said

Miss Toms – and then she gasped in surprise.

A figure had suddenly sprung up behind Mr Browser, grabbed him round the neck and pulled him down. The two bodies rolled out of sight on the other side of the ridge.

The children stared dumbly at the place where Mr Browser had stood, and Mrs Portland-Smythe gave a little cry and fainted away. This time Mr Portland-Smythe left her lying on the seat and made for the door.

'Where are you going?' demanded the pilot.

'Why, someone has to go and help him,' said the Chairman of the Parents' Association bravely. 'I brought him out here – it's my responsibility.'

'Nonsense!' declared the pilot. 'No one else leaves this plane unless I give the order. We can't afford to be picked off one by one. Our duty is to stay and protect the main party.'

'Poor Mr Browser,' said Anna Cardwell, and she began to cry.

'Cheer up, you silly girl,' said Miss Toms instantly. 'There was no shot. He may have been taken prisoner. When he tells them why we're here, maybe they will send help.'

But it was clear to all that Miss Toms was putting on a brave face, and there was silence in the plane, the only movement being made by Mr Portland-Smythe, who was fanning his wife's face with a handkerchief.

The sun was now shining directly on the plane and the passengers mopped their brows as the temperature rose and they began to perspire. The air hostess brought round drinks, but as the refrigerator was not working they were lukewarm, and did little to help quench thirsts or cool the passengers down.

'Hot tea would be better,' said the pilot to Mr Portland-Smythe. 'It helps the body perspire, and after that you feeler cooler. But we'd better keep that until later, when the sun is even hotter. There's a distinct danger that some will suffer from prickly heat and others from heat exhaustion. I wish I knew why the electrics won't work. It's a mystery to me.'

'If it grows too hot, can't we all come out of the plane and shelter under its wings?' suggested Miss Toms.

'Good idea,' replied the pilot. 'We may be forced to do so later, but I'm more afraid that we may be being watched by hostile tribesmen, in which case it would be fatal to come out of the plane.'

'I'm fed up!' called out Anna. 'I want to go home!'

The other passengers looked at her, and to their surprise she had recovered her spirits and was now laughing, not crying. A number of the others joined in her laughter – but their laughs were nervous and there was little amusement in their eyes. Anna had put into words the truth that was dawning upon them; they couldn't go home, and if the worst happened, they might never see home again.

6

Mr Browser is Captured

When Mr Browser stopped on his climb to tie knots
in his handkerchief and put it over his head, he was
not very optimistic that it would do him much
good, and he wished he still had the pith helmet
which had served him so well many years ago. He
climbed onwards, sensing once again the special
smell of the hard, cracked ground, and recalling
that apart from hostile tribesmen there were other
dangers to be reckoned with, such as sunstroke,
snake bites and even perhaps the risk of being bitten
by a malarial mosquito.

Spiky and Michael would be completely unaware
of all these possibilities, and might easily tread
where they ought not to do; to contact them was a
matter of urgency. He was perspiring freely and had
to take off his glasses and wipe them clean just
before he reached the summit.

To his great delight, when he stood at the top, he
caught a glimpse of the boys away to his right. They
were approaching some bushes, and he prepared to
call to them, for in bushes lay danger. Before he
could open his mouth, an arm was thrust around his
neck like a rod of iron, and he fell to the ground.

choking. As soon as he touched the ground, the arm left his neck and was used to assist his captor in pinning both Mr Browser's arms behind him. Expertly the attacker frisked his pockets, and when he found no weapons on his victim, he eased the pressure on his arms.

'Help!' gasped Mr Browser. 'Let me up!'

There was a slight pause, perhaps while his captor puzzled over his prisoner's English. Then, to Mr Browser's surprise, he answered in the same language.

'No weapon?' he demanded.

'No,' said Mr Browser thankfully.

'Have knife and rifle,' said the tribesman. 'You not run away!'

'No,' agreed Mr Browser.

'Stand up!'

Mr Browser obeyed, and saw opposite him a wiry little tribesman, a Pathan with a leathery, wrinkled face. He had a grey puggaree wound round his head and was wearing baggy brown trousers and sandals. Slung around him was a bandolier, no doubt full of ammunition, and he was holding his rifle so that at any moment he could shoot.

Thoughts from the past whirled through Mr Browser's mind. This man could well be a Mirali, a tribe at times friendly to white people – or a Razir, who would be likely to be hostile. Mr Browser looked into the little man's eyes, and noticed the greying hair at his temples. As he gazed, the expression on the tribesman's lean face changed from watchfulness to wonderment.

'Browser Sahib? It is you? You have come back?'

Mr Browser stared confusedly.

'Browser Sahib – for six months Iqbal Khan your bearer in Rawalpindi.'

Iqbal Kahn! He had been but a boy in those months when Mr Browser was stationed in Rawalpindi. Take away the grey hairs, the wrinkles on the face and the skin grown leathery under the sun – and there was, indeed, Iqbal Khan! Mr Browser stretched out his hand, intending to shake hands with his old servant, but Iqbal was a man of tradition. He put down his rifle and saluted, just as he had done in the past, with just a touch of mockery in the salute, so Mr Browser had always believed.

'Old man now, Sahib!'

Iqbal was referring to himself, though in fact, according to Mr Browser's calculations, he must still be between forty and fifty.

'You come in plane, Sahib?'

'Yes. And did you fire on it, Iqbal?'

'Yes, Sahib. Two shots. To warn my friends; they will be here shortly. Life is still hard here, Browser Sahib. We cannot tell whose plane that might be.

Afghanistan not far – no good, Sahib.'

'I suppose not.'

'You lucky – Razirs over next hill. Still bad men, all Razirs. Greedy, attacking Miralis when they can. Razirs may come to attack your plane.'

Mr Browser, having survived this crisis, remembered Spiky and Michael.

'Iqbal,' he asked, 'have you seen two boys?'

'Yes, Sahib. Your boys? I see them, and think to follow them, then I see you come from plane.'

'You wouldn't have shot them, Iqbal, would you?'

'No, Sahib. Only capture.'

Quite likely, thought Mr Browser, Iqbal and his friends would not have been above kidnapping the boys. He made a quick decision.

'Those boys my sons,' he said. 'More children are in the plane. We must have help to save these children. The sun is too hot.'

'Yes, Sahib. Sun too hot and Razirs too bad. Miralis will protect your sons.'

'Good – then let's try and find those two boys.'

They hadn't moved far to the right when Spiky and Michael came running towards them. When they saw Mr Browser, they accelerated, but did not call out. Only when they were puffing and panting by Mr Browser's side did they speak.

'Mr Browser – a terrible thing has happened!'

began Spiky.

'Terrible? You've been lucky so far,' Mr Browser greeted them. 'You could have been shot. Luckily this is my old bearer, Iqbal Kahn. You are safe, now.'

'No, Mr Browser, no!' called out Michael hysterically. 'Down in the hollow over there – something terrible has landed.'

'Landed?'

'Yes, Mr Browser. It's the Brain Sharpeners. They've come back. They've landed in that hollow, in a simply huge pepperpotty thing. And Mr Salt's been to see them!'

'Mr Salt?'

'Yes,' declared Spiky. 'I reckon Mr Salt has brought us out here so that he can hand us over to the Brain Sharpeners. Otherwise, why would he visit them secretly?'

'Not understand,' put in Iqbal. Mr Browser looked critically at the boys.

'Are you sure you know what you're talking about?' he asked. 'The sun is very strong out here, and maybe what you saw was a mist formation rising from a pool. Maybe you're suffering from a mild touch of the sun –'

'Please, Mr Browser,' begged Spiky, 'don't waste time – just come and look. But don't go too close, or show yourself.'

74

Iqbal advanced with Mr Browser, his rifle at the ready.

'No shooting, Iqbal,' Mr Browser ordered. 'I think these boys have been seeing things, but let's make sure.'

'Hot sun not good for white men,' pronounced Iqbal, and he took the lead as they advanced towards the bushes. Mr Browser saw that Spiky and Michael were hanging back, anxious for him to see what was in the hollow, but far from keen to view it again for themselves. As he followed Iqbal, he thought hard about the mysterious return of Mr Salt to Chivvy Chase School after he had been supposed to have had a nervous breakdown. Secretly Mr Browser had doubted that story; Mr Salt's disappearance after going out on the school field suggested strongly to him that the Brain Sharpeners had taken charge of him. When he returned, Mr Browser supposed that they had released him as worthless to them. Now he had to reckon with the possibility that Mr Salt was still in their power, under their influence –

'Sahib!' Iqbal Khan had stretched out behind a bush, his rifle resting on the ground in front of him. He was staring through a gap, down into the hollow. 'It is a god, Sahib, come down to this land!'

Iqbal turned to look anxiously at Mr Browser, and his dark skin paled with fright. Mr Browser

peered over Iqbal's shoulder, and his pink skin was drained of blood as quickly as Iqbal's. The sight of the huge pepperpot induced in Mr Browser a kind of daylight nightmare; he lived again his first acquaintance with the Brain Sharpeners, and trembled at the recollection of how they had possessed his brain until Michael Fairlie had managed to save him and Class 8 from the Brain Sharpeners' attentions.

He ducked away and pulled Iqbal back.

'That's not a god, Iqbal, it's an enemy who wishes to capture all my children. We must keep away, or the Brain Sharpeners will take charge of us too!'

'Brain Sharpeners, Sahib? I will shoot them – '

'No, no, Iqbal. We must stop the children from going with them.'

'But Mr Salt has gone back to the plane,' whispered Spiky. 'He will persuade them to come to the pepperpot. Perhaps they are already in the power of Mr Salt!'

Mr Browser muttered something – for Spiky had expressed his own fears; the Headmaster had probably been under the influence of the Brain Sharpeners ever since he returned to Chivvy Chase School. They had sent him back with the express purpose of capturing the children, and he had arranged to bring Class 8 to this remote spot so that they could carry out their plans without being seen by any suspicious

77

people. Perhaps they even planned to take the adults with them as well, so that no human being would remain to tell the story of why the children had vanished. Mr Browser groaned aloud.

'What's the matter, Mr Browser?' asked Michael. 'Can't we go back to the plane?'

'No,' said Mr Browser firmly – and then turned to Iqbal, who was on his feet again as they retreated from the hollow. 'Iqbal, you and your Miralis are my only hope. You say your friends are coming?'

'Yes, Sahib, they will come.'

'Then they must stop the children from entering that white tower we have just seen. How long will they be?'

'Ten minutes, Sahib. Fifteen minutes. No hurry. My shots were a sign of something found, not warning of a battle.'

'Can't you fire again?' asked Spiky, but Iqbal shook his head.

'Friends already on way,' he declared, and suddenly broke into one of those broad smiles which Mr Browser remembered from the past.

'Come, Browser Sahib,' said Iqbal enthusiastically. 'I show you something which will frighten Razirs or Brain Sharpeners. Miralis have old cannon from long time back – hidden in cave on hill. Over there!'

He pointed to the highest point of the ridge,

further to the left, where some small trees hid the summit of the hill.

'But we must watch the plane – '

'From the cave we can watch plane, fire on Brain Sharpeners and Razirs, and stop your children from entering white tower.'

'All right, then,' agreed Mr Browser uneasily, and they followed Iqbal along the ridge on the far side of the plane.

'Does he think we are all your children?' asked Michael.

'Perhaps,' replied Mr Browser. 'But it doesn't matter as long as he and his friends try to help us.'

Iqbal moved along the side of the ridge so fast that even the boys had difficulty in keeping up with him, and soon Mr Browser was lagging behind, puffing and gasping. Suddenly Iqbal crossed the ridge and disappeared behind some low bushes. The boys followed, and Mr Browser struggled after them. For a moment, before he too disappeared behind the bushes, he caught a glimpse of the plane down below, glittering in the sunshine. Then an arm shot out and pulled him through an opening in the hillside, and into the mouth of a small cave.

Two tribesmen dressed in similar clothes to Iqbal were staring at Spiky and Michael as if they were visitors from another planet. Iqbal chattered away to his friends in his native Pushtu tongue,

79

while Mr Browser stared amazed at an object standing behind them. It was a large cannon, with a few cannonballs lying on the ground beside it.

'Old cannon, Browser Sahib, captured by Miralis in an old battle. Now it can help us, perhaps, yes?'

Mr Browser was not very optimistic about the chances of an old cannon driving the Brain Sharpeners away, but he didn't like to upset Iqbal's enthusiasm. They sat down at a table at the end of the cave, and Mr Browser began the difficult task of explaining to his old servant and his friends Fazal and Akbar how he came to be in their territory again.

'You have twenty children?' said Iqbal in admiration. 'It is an honour that you bring them to our land. But we have two enemies, Sahib. The things in the white tower, and perhaps the Razirs. If they find the plane, they will attack and capture it for money. Bad men, the Razirs!'

Mr Browser was not too sure the Miralis were much better, but at least he had the Miralis on his side.

'Making plan to use cannon,' Iqbal explained after more chatter. 'Cannon will destroy white tower and frighten Razirs. Your children shall be safe, if twenty Razirs have to die!'

With the Brain Sharpeners on his mind, Mr Browser was not inclined to worry much about the Razirs.

'Spiky and Michael,' he said, 'you'd better keep watch on the plane, and let us know if there's any sign of the passengers coming out of it. This old cannon won't be much use against the Brain Sharpeners. We must stop Mr Salt from persuading the children to go into the hollow, if that's what he's trying to do. Once they are there, the Brain Sharpeners will take over!'

'We'll keep watch, Mr Browser,' declared Spiky, and the boys moved to the entrance of the cave and peered out between the bushes at the stranded plane beneath them.

'It must be growing dreadfully hot in there,' said Michael, watching the sun shimmering on the wings and body of the plane.

'Mr Browser was right,' admitted Spiky, 'the heat's pretty terrific here in the daytime.'

'That's it!' said Michael, clenching his fists.

'That's what?'

'That's how Mr Salt will persuade them to come out. They'll all be gasping for air and perspiring and suffering from thirst, and he'll tell them how cool and pleasant it is under the trees in the hollow. Not true, of course, but they'll listen to him and they'll be glad to follow him.'

'That could be right,' agreed Spiky. 'Mike – perhaps you've helped to stop the Brain Sharpeners again!'

'But how can we stop them? If the passengers come out of the plane, we can't let these tribesmen shoot at them, and Mr Salt will just keep going.'

'Someone,' declared Spiky, like a general making a big decision in a battle, 'must get down there and warn them – delay them until there are enough Miralis to surround the hollow.'

'Let's tell Mr Browser –'

'No! No time for that. Let him go on planning with his friend Iqbal; he might not allow anyone to go if we talked to him about it. I'm going to run down there at once. I'll be there in five minutes – it's downhill nearly all the way.'

'You boys,' came the voice of Mr Browser, 'have you seen anything yet?'

'No – no movement yet!' Michael called out. He looked behind him, and saw that the Miralis were painfully pushing the cannon towards the mouth of the cave.

'You keep Mr Browser informed while I run for it,' said Spiky, and stood up ready to go.

'Take care!' Michael warned him. 'Don't break your leg.'

'See you!' said Spiky, and bursting through the bushes he started to run downhill.

Michael watched tensely. Spiky could so easily lose his balance – he was gaining speed all the time and could trip over a stone or a crack in the dry ground. Yet at the same time Michael envied him because he was going back to all his friends on the plane.

Iqbal appeared, and scrambled over the top of the ridge, then hurried back.

'More Miralis coming from village,' he announced happily. 'Now Razirs will have trouble if they come.'

'It's the Brain Sharpeners I'm worried about,' Mr Browser could not help saying.

'Brain Sharpeners – don't know,' said Iqbal bluntly.

'All quiet, boys?' asked Mr Browser.

'All quiet,' replied Michael, but Iqbal was an old soldier not easily to be tricked. He looked sharply at Michael, then down the hill.

'One boy running to plane,' he declared. 'Very dangerous. Razirs could shoot.'

'Oh, Spiky, how could you be so foolish!' complained Mr Browser, and Michael showed surprise that Mr Browser had used the nickname 'Spiky' and not called him Simon as he usually did. He tried to defend his friend.

'He's gone to warn the others not to follow Mr Salt,' he said. 'Someone has to stop them leaving the plane.'

'That's true,' agreed Mr Browser.

'Fire – to tell him to come back?' asked Iqbal.

'No, no. Let him go,' decided Mr Browser.

'Quick boy,' admitted Iqbal as Spiky slipped and slithered down the last part of the hill. No more was said as they watched Spiky's progress towards the prisoners in the plane.

7
Mr Salt's Return

The temperature in the plane rose each minute as the sun beat down upon it. Even Miss Toms had droplets of perspiration on her forehead.

'Please, Miss, can't we go outside?' pleaded Anna. 'It's worse than a greenhouse in here.'

'I know it's hot,' replied Miss Toms, 'but we must do what the pilot wishes. He knows best.'

'If we stay in here all day we shall be frizzled to nothing,' declared Selwyn. 'The sun won't be going

down for at least eight hours, and it hasn't reached full strength yet – '

'Be quiet, Selwyn!' ordered Miss Toms. 'No doubt something will happen soon.'

'But what, Miss Toms?' asked Anna. Miss Toms frowned and refused to answer any more questions, but shortly afterwards she moved up the plane to talk to Mr Portland-Smythe, who was doing his best to calm down his wife.

'I can't stand this heat much longer,' the distressed lady was muttering. Miss Toms drew Mr Portland-Smythe to one side.

'Some of the children are suffering,' she whispered. 'I'm afraid they'll be ill if we don't escape from this sun trap. Can't you persuade the pilot to let us shelter beneath the plane?'

'He's afraid there'll be shooting,' admitted the Chairman. 'He doesn't want to expose the children to danger.'

'He'll soon be exposing them to danger if they stay here,' Miss Toms warned him. 'Sooner or later we'll have to take the risk.'

'I'm inclined to agree,' said Mr Portland-Smythe. 'I'll go and have a word with him.'

The pilot was still busily trying to make contact with the outside world.

'It's most mysterious,' he said, mopping his brow with a paper towel. 'The apparatus is dead as a doornail, yet there are no dust storms nor thunderstorms anywhere near.'

'They want to leave the plane,' explained Mr Portland-Smythe. 'Miss Toms is afraid some of them won't stand the heat much longer.'

'If she's afraid, then there must be something in it,' said the pilot. 'To tell you the truth, I'm not very comfortable myself. I suppose we'll have to take the risk. Mr Browser should never have gone without a weapon. At least we'll be able to fire back at the tribesmen if they shoot at us. We'll find as much cover as we can behind the plane, and hope that they won't encircle us.'

Mr Portland-Smythe was just returning to the other passengers when Selwyn Jordan suddenly shouted out loud.

'Miss Toms – it's Mr Salt! He's coming back down the hill, and he doesn't look hurt at all!'

Mr Portland-Smythe joined the others at the windows. Mr Salt was striding purposefully down the hill towards the plane, and the sight of him filled the passengers with hope. No one was shooting at him, and he had not been captured. Maybe everything was going to be all right after all; they would be able to leave the terrible, stifling atmosphere of the plane, and perhaps Spiky and Michael were safe as well. Even Mr Browser might have persuaded his attacker to set him free.

Anna started waving to Mr Salt, and the others joined in with her. After a minute or two, Mr Salt saw them and waved stiffly back, and the children cheered. Suddenly they forgot the heat, their thirst and the stickiness of their clothes as they peered out to catch the expression on the Headmaster's face as he drew nearer. He started to cross the dry river bed, and when he looked up and saw their faces at the windows, he smiled and waved to them again.

'He's happy,' said Anna joyfully. 'He's probably seen a village, and they'll be sending help for us.'

'Maybe he's found somewhere for us to shelter,' said Mrs Portland-Smythe hopefully.

Mr Salt was helped aboard the plane, and the pilot and Mr Portland-Smythe expected him to come to them privately and give a report on what he had found, but he turned away from them towards the rest of the passengers.

'Children,' he began, 'it's terribly hot in here.' They agreed. 'But I'm pleased to tell you that there is no need to stay here a moment longer. I have come from a place near the top of that hill,' – he pointed out of the window nearest him – 'where there are bushes and shade, and even a small stream running. There you will be able to rest during the heat of the day, until such time as you are rescued.'

'Three cheers for Mr Salt!' called out Martin, and the children cheered as though it were the end of the school year.

'You're all looking hot and bothered,' went on Mr Salt. 'There's no reason for delay – we should start as soon as possible, or you'll begin to suffer from heatstroke.'

'Yes, let's go!' called out Anna, and stood up ready to start.

'One moment!' The pilot stood between them and the door. 'What about the shooting?' he asked Mr Salt. 'We can't take any risks.'

'Shooting?' replied the Headmaster irritably. 'I haven't heard any. And I've just walked down the hillside in full view of anyone who wanted to shoot at me, and there wasn't a shot fired. I see no danger at all.'

'Nevertheless, someone did shoot at the plane,' insisted the pilot.

'Are you sure?' asked Mr Salt. 'Maybe you imagined it. Or perhaps somebody fired a couple of passing shots and went away. One thing is certain – if you don't remove these children soon from this oven, they'll all collapse from the heat. I shall lead the children out myself, if you don't wish to come.'

Mr Salt spoke as he often did at school, in tones which no one could dare to ignore. To disobey him would have been unthinkable.

'It's quite true,' said Miss Toms. 'We can't stay in

here much longer. I propose that the adults go in front and make a shield for the children, so that if there is any shooting they will be protected, and some of us can fire back.'

'Let us go, please,' begged Anna. 'It's growing hotter and hotter.'

'Why are we delaying?' asked Mrs Portland-Smythe.

The pilot weighed up the situation, then nodded to Miss Toms.

'We'll have to risk it,' he agreed. Most of the passengers were now concentrating on leaving the plane, but Selwyn Jordan happened to glance out of the window.

'Look!' he shouted. 'Someone else is coming down the hill!'

A small figure was hurtling, almost tumbling, down the hillside further over to their left, making for the plane. Miss Toms quietly took out her pistol.

'It's Spiky!' called out Anna.

'So it is,' agreed Miss Toms, slipping the pistol away again. 'I wonder what's happened to Michael. We'd better wait for Simon Jackson, Mr Salt.'

Mr Salt looked far from pleased.

'That boy always was a nuisance,' he grumbled. 'Let's start off, and he can join us.'

Spiky was now running across the river bed

towards them.

'Move on!' ordered Mr Salt.

'No – wait!' countermanded the pilot. 'We can't desert the others. Maybe this boy can tell us what has happened to them.'

'Ridiculous!' muttered Mr Salt, fearful lest the Brain Sharpeners should be growing impatient. 'He won't be able to tell us anything, if I know him. We ought not to waste a second.'

'You seem to be in a great hurry,' commented the pilot, and Mr Salt made no answer.

Spiky, his shirt stained with sweat, staggered the last few metres to the plane and was pulled into it, where he stood gasping.

'Spiky – where's Michael?' called out Anna. Miss Toms thrust a damp handkerchief into Spiky's hand so that he could at least cool his face a little.

'Michael and Mr Browser are both safe at the moment,' Spiky blurted out.

'Well, that's good news,' declared Mr Portland-Smythe. 'So everybody's safe. Thank goodness for that!'

'Yes – but we're all in awful danger!' added Spiky.

'All of us? What do you mean?' the pilot asked him.

'It's the Brain Sharpeners,' said Spiky. 'They're here, up near the top of the hill, and they're waiting for us.'

When they heard the words 'Brain Sharpeners', the passengers were at once divided into two groups – the children, who knew about them but never spoke of them, just as bad nightmares soon tend to be forgotten and are never spoken of, and the rest of the passengers who were entirely unaware of their existence, except, of course, for Mr Salt. So the children sat silent and confused, and the adults looked suspiciously at Spiky.

'Brain Sharpeners?' said the pilot, and turned to Miss Toms for an explanation, as if he believed that Spiky might be talking in some strange, secret school code.

Spiky gazed earnestly at Miss Toms, wondering if Mr Browser had confided in her about the Brain Sharpeners. But he received no comfort from Miss Toms.

'Brain Sharpeners? Whatever are you talking about, Simon?' she demanded in her strict no nonsense voice.

'Mr Browser knows, Miss,' Spiky began to plead – but Mr Salt cut him short.

'The boy is talking nonsense,' he said. 'Clearly he has been affected by the sun. We had better take him with us into the shade as soon as possible.'

'No! No!' cried Spiky. 'We mustn't go outside, or we shall come under their influence. They want to take us away to another world, where they'll sharpen our brains and use us to colonise one of their planets. We'll be slaves, Miss Toms, honest we will! They've tried before, and now they've brought us out here so that no one will know where we've gone or what has happened to us. We shall simply disappear – '

'Rubbish, boy!' snapped Mr Salt. 'The only danger to us comes from the sun, and possibly a wandering tribesman or two. Please, Miss Toms, organise the children to leave the plane. We must get up to our shady hollow as quickly as we can!'

'No! No! That's just the place where the Brain Sharpeners are,' cried Spiky. 'I've seen them there– and Mr Salt's in league with them. They took him away with them, and while he was away they probably worked on his brain!'

'What cheek!' said Mr Portland-Smythe, who, like the rest of the Parents' Association officials, was under the impression that Mr Salt had been absent because he had suffered a nervous breakdown. They knew that Miss Toms had taken over the school until he recovered.

'How can you be so rude, Simon!' said Miss Toms angrily. 'You mustn't ever talk about your Headmaster like that!'

'I'm not rude,' protested Spiky, who was now near to tears. 'He's in the power of the Brain

Sharpeners, I know he is. I saw him coming out of their pepperpot thing.'

'Pepperpot? The boy must be suffering from advanced sunstroke,' decided Mr Portland-Smythe; but the word 'pepperpot' brought memories flooding back to Anna Cardwell.

'That's right!' she called out. 'Spiky's right. The first time they came, it was in a kind of pepperpot thing.'

'And this one's ten times as big!' declared Spiky gratefully.

'Ridiculous!' said Mr Salt. 'The heat is getting to them all, Miss Toms. This is the beginning of hysteria. They'll all start imagining things, unless we bring them out of this oven.'

Memories were stirring in more than one mind, and the children looked scared and uneasy.

'Please!' shouted Spiky, as Mr Salt moved to the door. 'Don't go with him. Can't you see he looks very odd? The Brain Sharpeners are in control of him, and I expect they arranged for us to crash here. Mr Salt fixed all this – please believe me!'

Spiky felt like someone who is trying to persuade the Flat Earth Society that the world is round. The harder he tried, the more they were inclined to think that he was suffering from the effects of the sun. And when he told them in addition about how Mr Browser had met up with his old servant, Iqbal, and that Iqbal was ready to help defy the Brain Sharpeners and Mr Salt, that was the final straw.

The Class 8 passengers, suffering from the heat and now also from worry about Spiky's report, were near to collapsing, and the pilot decided he could delay no longer.

'Lead on, Mr Salt,' he ordered, 'and Miss Toms, please see that the passengers follow as quickly as possible. The adults must go first to try and shield the children from any attack.'

'But the Brain Sharpeners!' begged Spiky. 'What about them?'

The pilot gave him a knowing look.

'We'll deal with them when we see them,' he said. 'Mr Salt – lead on!'

Mr Salt needed no encouragement. He leaped out of the plane, and when he turned to see that the rest were following, there was a triumphant smile on his face.

'I think Spiky could be right, Miss Toms,' whispered Anna. 'There's something funny about Mr Salt.'

Miss Toms did not answer her, but she did give Mr Salt one of her sharpest looks. Soon all the passengers were out of the plane, and with the adults spread out ahead of them, Mr Salt's procession to the top of the hill began. He kept on moving impatiently ahead, then turning and urging

them on.

'Phew! It's just as hot out here as inside the plane!' complained Selwyn. 'Mr Browser was right – you could fry an egg on these stones.'

'Keep going!' Mr Salt encouraged them. 'We'll soon be there.'

Spiky Jackson trudged miserably and reluctantly at the end of the line of children. Anna dropped back gradually to speak to him.

'Are you sure about the Brain Sharpeners, Spiky?'

'Of course I am. Could I ever forget them? I tell you, Anna, when we reach the top of the hill I shall run away, back to Mr Browser in the cave, if I have the strength.'

'I'll come with you,' declared Anna.

'Hurry up, you two at the back – don't lag behind!' came the voice of Mr Salt from the front, and Miss Toms dropped back a little to shepherd them along.

Suddenly a burst of gunfire came from somewhere along the top of the hill.

'What's that?' cried Mrs Portland-Smythe in a panic.

'It could be the Razirs,' muttered Spiky. 'If it is, we're in the middle of a tribal battle as well as being on our way to the Brain Sharpeners. Oh, how I wish I'd never come!'

'And I,' agreed Anna.

'Speed up!' cried Mr Salt. 'Once we're in the shade of the bushes, we'll be safe.'

'I wonder,' observed Miss Toms, looking doubtful for the first time.

8
The Pepperpot God

Michael Fairlie, still left on guard after watching
Spiky vanish into the plane, was soon joined by the
mouth of the cannon, as Iqbal's friends pushed and
pulled it out with frequent grunts and groans. They
were turning the cannon into position so that it
could be fired in the direction of the pepperpot,
when there came a burst of shooting.

'What's that?' asked Mr Browser nervously.

'It is perhaps my friends who have met some

Razirs on their way and fired on them, or it is the Razirs who have fired on my friends,' said Iqbal, frowning. 'It is bad if the Razirs are here, Browser Sahib. Bad men!'

'I know that,' said Mr Browser wearily. 'What can we do?'

'I will find my friends coming from the village,' said Iqbal. 'I tell them not to fight the Razirs yet. I find out where these Razirs are.'

'Good,' said Mr Browser, though he still had his mind on the Brain Sharpeners and the children.

Iqbal disappeared through the bushes, and his friends in the cave began loading the cannon.

'Mr Browser,' whispered Michael. 'Mr Salt is out of the plane, and the rest are following him. I can see the pilot, and Miss Toms. They're all coming, Mr Browser!'

'Oh dear!' was the only comment Mr Browser could make as he tried to work out how they could possibly escape from the twin perils of the Brain Sharpeners and the Razirs.

'You must be ready to hide at the back of the cave, Michael, in case the Razirs come,' he said – but almost as soon as he had finished speaking some tribesmen burst in on them from the other side of the ridge.

'Inside, Michael!' yelled Mr Browser – but Fazal and Akbar stopped him.

'Miralis,' explained Fazal, and welcomed his fellow tribesmen.

'Where are the Razirs?' asked Mr Browser.

None of the tribesmen spoke English, but several of them repeated the word 'Razirs' and shrugged their shoulders. There were now twelve Miralis crowded at the mouth of the cave. They were speaking to one another in their own language, and once or twice Michael thought he heard the name 'Iqbal'. With Mr Browser he looked down again at the plane, and saw the children forming up ready to start to climb the hill.

'He's persuaded them to come!' said Michael sadly. 'Can't we warn them to stop?'

'If Spiky couldn't do it, we might not be able to,' said Mr Browser. 'All we would do is reveal our position. We must wait and hope that Iqbal and his friends can stop them.'

At that point Iqbal dashed into the middle of them as if out of nowhere.

'Browser Sahib,' he said, grinning as he panted for breath, 'is that white tower a god?'

'A god? Of course not,' said Mr Browser. 'It's from another world, but it's not a god.'

'You are sure, Sahib?'

'Certain, Iqbal. I give you my word.'

Iqbal doubled up with laughter.

'Then come and see what the stupid Razirs are

doing,' he said, and slapped his thigh hard with his hand to show extreme amusement. 'Come,' he repeated, and Mr Browser had his arm tugged at to persuade him to go.

'May I come too?' asked Michael, unwilling to be left with the Miralis.

'Is it safe?' asked Mr Browser.

'Safe – very safe,' Iqbal replied.

They crept along the side of the ridge hidden from the plane until they reached the rim of the hollow. Iqbal knelt down and fell forward in order to peer over the rim, and Mr Browser and Michael copied him.

In the hollow, all around the giant pepperpot, about forty Razir tribesmen were kneeling and bowing down to it, their noses touching the dusty ground as they worshipped the mysterious white tower. After a few seconds, Iqbal signalled to Mr Browser and Michael to withdraw.

'They think it's a god,' said Michael.

'Yes, but we still don't know what the Brain Sharpeners will do,' said Mr Browser. 'Look, Iqbal, the children are coming up the hill. We must stop them!'

'Yes, Browser Sahib. Miralis will surround them and stop them.

'But no firing,' pleaded Mr Browser. 'Don't fire on anyone, whatever happens.'

Iqbal looked disappointed, but then cheered up again. 'We will fire the cannon at the white tower,' he said. 'Then the Razirs will think their god is angry.' He slipped away without waiting for a reply. Mr Browser took up a position from which they could watch Mr Salt's procession rather than the Razirs. Mr Salt was now clearly to be seen, more than halfway up the hill.

Suddenly the Miralis appeared and spread out between the children and the top of the hill, their rifles at the ready. Mr Salt stopped in surprise, and the procession behind him, with adults on either side of it, halted too. Mr Salt gave the situation a moment's thought – or appeared to do so – then waved the procession on vigorously. Spiky Jackson, right at the back, appeared to be waving to his friends to go the other way. Mr Salt strode on, the rest shuffled on doubtfully.

'I'm going down the hill to warn them,' decided Mr Browser – but as he made to move there came a roar and a whoosh and a bang. The Miralis had fired the cannon.

Mr Salt burst through the ranks of the Miralis on the hill, who closed together to impede the children, who were still following. Mr Salt disappeared over the top of the hollow, and Mr Browser, seeing the children stop, turned his attention to the hollow. Michael followed him and peered over. He watched

102

fascinated. The first cannonball must have landed just in front of the doorway of the pepperpot, and now a second one crashed into its side. The Razirs, now hopelessly incapable of facing up to the situation, not knowing why their new god was angry, were lying face down on the ground. Iqbal danced about with joy, never having seen his old enemies grovelling on the ground before.

Mr Salt ran through their ranks toward the open doorway. No children were following him, for the Miralis had stopped them, and Miss Toms had now decided that it would be wiser to go no further. The door of the pepperpot began to close. Mr Salt was frantically trying to reach the narrowing opening, but he was too late. He banged with his fists on the sides of the pepperpot, but the Brain Sharpeners wanted no more of him. The whirring sound with which Michael Fairlie was familiar began again, only much louder because this pepperpot was so much bigger. Mr Salt fell forward as if struck by some invisible ray.

'Down! Out of sight!' yelled Mr Browser, and pulled Michael and Iqbal back from the edge of the hollow. The Razirs, some getting to their feet, watched as their god began to rise from the ground. Then the same invisible force which had attacked Mr Salt felled them too. They lay unconscious on the ground as the pepperpot rose in a stately climb

103

out of the hollow.

Then a dense dust storm arose, so thick that all those in the area had to hide their heads and close their eyes against the driving dust. When it stopped rising, Mr Browser rushed down to the children and urged them back into the plane.

'There's still danger from hostile tribesmen,' he warned them.

'Where's Mr Salt?' demanded the pilot.

'Never mind Mr Salt – back into the plane as quickly as you can!' shouted Mr Portland-Smythe. 'Mr Salt persuaded me to arrange all this, so he can find his own way back.'

'We can't leave him to the Razirs,' objected Mr Browser. 'They can be a cruel lot – I'll go back and see whether Iqbal or I can help him. Michael's still up there, too.'

'I'll come back with you,' shouted Spiky, and ran after Mr Browser before anyone could stop him.

The scene in the hollow, which was being watched with great curiosity and wonder by Iqbal and his fellow Mirali tribesmen, was chaotic. The pepperpot was gone, leaving exposed bare rock beneath it where it had blown the surface earth away on taking off. Mr Salt was lying motionless where he had fallen, and the Razir tribesmen were gradually picking themselves up and staggering about like drunken men. Some of them clutched their heads with their hands, others sheltered their eyes with their arms, afraid lest the angry pepperpot god should return.

'Could shoot them all,' observed Iqbal with great satisfaction.

'No, no,' Mr Browser pleaded with him. 'There's no need to do that. You won't have much more trouble from them for a while – they think the Brain Sharpeners are angry with them, and that the white tower was something to do with the Miralis. Look – they are starting to run away!'

The Razirs, as if returning to consciousness, were calling out to one another, pointing to the body of Mr Salt and then starting a retreat from the hollow. Soon they had all disappeared, leaving Iqbal and his men confused to see such tough fighters running away like frightened children. If the Razirs were so frightened of the white tower, the Miralis had their doubts too; what if the Brain Sharpeners came back and attacked them? So they refused to move an inch to the help of Mr Salt, and only when Mr Browser and Michael ran towards him did Iqbal timorously follow.

The Headmaster was lying face downwards, and when Mr Browser turned him over, Mr Salt began mumbling to himself. The words were disjointed, as if received telegram style from some outside source. Mr Salt was repeating a message which must have been transmitted to him by the Commander of the departed pepperpot.

'You have failed the Brain Sharpeners. You have exposed us to too many people, and we could not allow the other adults to return with tales about us. The world would be on guard against us, so that it would become impossible to remove further children secretly. Your planet is too dangerous. I must report back, as Commander, the failure of my second mission. I shall not be given another chance, and the Brain Sharpeners will probably never return in the hope of gaining population for colonisation. Only, perhaps, to stop the mental progress of your world should you become clever enough to threaten us. As for you, we have no further use for you. This is our revenge – when we are gone, your brain will never work as it did before. You will remember nothing: your brain will be stunned for ever by the shock we shall now give you. Farewell for ever, Mr Salt – we are departing from your mind – we are departing from your mind –'

Mr Salt stopped speaking, and Mr Browser was about to lift him up when he began again to recite the same message that he had just finished, like an answering machine.

'You have failed the Brain Sharpeners. You have exposed us to too many people –'

The Brain Sharpeners were imposing their message on Mr Salt's subconscious.

'We must wake him up,' said Mr Browser, and lifted the Headmaster into a sitting position. 'The Brain Sharpeners have gone, Mr Salt,' he shouted into his ear. Mr Salt stopped mumbling and opened his eyes.

'Where am I?' he asked. 'What happened to me? Is it time for afternoon school? Why hasn't the bell been rung?'

'You're not in school, Mr Salt,' said Spiky. 'You're on a hill near Afghanistan.'

Mr Salt looked blankly at Spiky, then at Mr Browser. 'That's right,' said Mr Browser. 'You were trying to take the children – '

'Take the children?' interrupted Mr Salt hurriedly, as if afraid of what Mr Browser might be going to say. 'I went for a walk to see if I could find help, and the sun was very hot, and suddenly I became very dizzy. It must have been sunstroke, I think. Yes, of course, the children in the plane were suffering from the sun, too. I found a sheltered place for them – but it was too late. Dear me – I do feel very odd!'

And Mr Salt's eyes flickered once or twice and then closed again.

'We must bring him to the plane,' said Mr Browser. 'Iqbal – give me a hand.'

'You take rifle, Sahib, I take body,' responded

108

Iqbal, and passed his rifle to Mr Browser. Then he bent low, heaved Mr Salt's body over his own, stood up and staggered off down the hill with the Headmaster on his back. Michael, Spiky and Mr Browser half walked, half trotted behind him, and so they went all the way to the plane. Mr Salt was manoeuvred up and placed on a reclining seat, where the air hostess did her best to revive him.

Suddenly the pilot hurried in from the front of the plane, more excited than he had ever been.

'The electrics are O.K. again,' he called out. 'I've just finished testing, and everything's in order. I'm going to see if I can start the engines up – they might be working again too. I can't understand why, but

everything seems normal again, as if by magic!'

He disappeared again, and in a few minutes an increasing roar told them the engines were firing again.

'Marvellous!' said Mr Portland-Smythe. 'It must have been the electric storms which put them out of action.'

'No, it was the –' began Spiky, but Mr Browser interrupted him.

'That's good,' he said. 'At least we can inform Rawalpindi and Karachi of where we are. But we surely can't fly out of here even if the engines are working. There are too many stones in the way. We shall have to wait for help.'

The pilot appeared again, and confirmed that all was in order.

'If only we had a decent runway, we wouldn't have to wait for help,' he said. 'They'll come with lorries to take us away, and that will take hours. Mr Salt is in bad shape, and the rest of the passengers aren't too good, in spite of the air conditioning being in working order again. I wish we could fly.'

'Perhaps we can,' suggested Spiky. 'Maybe we could clear a way for the plane by taking away all the larger stones in its path. We could make you a runway. If you could land here at night, you should be able to take off in daylight.'

'I think I could turn the plane and take off in the

direction from which we came,' said the pilot, 'but there are lots of stones which could cause trouble.'

'Perhaps Iqbal and his men would help too,' suggested Mr Browser. 'Together we could do it.'

'It's worth a try,' agreed the pilot – and out came the passengers again. Joining with the Miralis, and under instructions from the pilot, they began heaving and rolling stones away on a path worked out for the plane's take-off. It was hot and thirsty work, and occasionally some of the passengers would have to take a rest in the plane – but they worked with enthusiasm, none harder than Spiky and Michael.

'You were right about this place, Mr Browser,' said Spiky. 'It's hot enough to fry eggs here. Is it just as you remembered it?'

'Exactly,' said Mr Browser. 'If anything, worse. I'll be glad to be back in school.'

'So will I,' agreed Spiky.

'Yet you made it all sound so interesting when you were telling us about it, Mr Browser,' complained Anna.

The work went on until the worst obstacles for three hundred metres along the runway had been removed. Some boulders obstinately remained, but the pilot considered that he could avoid them, and the passengers once more returned to the plane. Before the engines could be started, there was Iqbal to be thought of.

'We ought to give him a present,' said Michael. 'In a way he saved our lives, with his cannon and his friends.'

'Excellent idea,' agreed Mr Portland-Smythe, who had overheard what had been said. 'Who has a hat? We'll send it round for him, and put in whatever we can spare. It need not be money – watches or jewellery would be acceptable, too.'

'Don't do it!' begged Mr Browser unexpectedly. 'No Pathan wants gifts for what he has done for a friend. He'll be insulted, and so will his friends, and there could be trouble. The Razirs may be bad men, but the Miralis aren't angels! We don't want to upset them at the last minute. We might even have a cannon fired at us. Pathans are proud people.'

The look in the watching Iqbal's eyes, as he stood at the door of the plane, helped to persuade Mr Portland-Smythe that perhaps this was another idea of his which was not so good after all, so the search for the hat was called off. Farewells were said, and Iqbal saluted everybody and honour was saved. The Miralis withdrew.

'Look after your children, Browser Sahib!' were Iqbal's final words before the engines started up and the seatbelts were fastened.

The take-off along the river bed was bumpy and a little scaring, but before the hills closed in the plane

rose and soared away over them, leaving the defeated and puzzled Razirs behind, wondering if their mysterious and cruel god would ever return to them.

A landing was made at Rawalpindi, where the passengers were treated for mild sunstroke and Mr Salt was taken away to hospital, because the poor man's mind seemed to have been unhinged by his long stay out in the sun. Nobody mentioned the Brain Sharpeners, either because they didn't wish to, or because the Brain Sharpeners themselves did not wish to remain in the memories of mere humans.

Parents back home, it was understood, were very

anxious to see their children again, and as those children had seen enough of tribal territory to last them for a long while, the holiday was cut short before it started. A couple of days later the party, minus poor Mr Salt, took off for home.

9
Return to Chivvy Chase

When the party arrived at the airport, joyful parents and curious reporters from the local and national press were there to receive them.

'You poor things!' said Spiky Jackson's mum. 'Why did they let you go out in the sun like that? They must have known you'd get sunstroke.'

'You look all right, lad,' said Spiky's dad. 'Had a touch of the Deolali tap, have you? Hello, Mr

Browser, glad to be 'ome again? Still mighty 'ot out there, is it?'

Mr Jackson was a cheerful ex-soldier who had put in some service out East, but most of the parents were much more concerned about their offspring. The press had been playing up the sunstroke angle, and questioning whether the Parents' Association should have taken the children so far away. One of the reporters managed to corner Michael Fairlie.

'Why did you leave the plane, if it was so hot outside?' she asked him.

'Because it was even hotter inside it,' said Michael. 'The air conditioning wasn't working.'

'How was it that your Headmaster was affected so much worse than the rest? Was he outside much longer?'

'Yes, he was.'

'Why was that?'

'Well, he said he was going to fetch help, but really he was going to meet the Brain Sharpeners – '

'Brain Sharpeners?'

Michael looked as confused as the reporter. The words had slipped out of his unconscious in an unguarded moment. Now the reporter was on the alert, licking the point of her pencil and flipping over to a clean page in her notebook.

'Well, really, of course, he came across some tribesmen, and they surrounded him – '

116

'Yes, but these Brain Sharpeners – who were they?'

'Oh, that was a nickname we gave to the tribesmen –'

'That's right,' called out Spiky. 'Just a nickname, it was.' Something inside them demanded that they keep quiet about the Brain Sharpeners.

'Must you worry these children any more?' put in Mrs Fairlie. 'You can see they're tired out, and they don't know what they're talking about. Maybe they're still suffering from the effects of the sun. It's not fair to question them like this.'

So the Brain Sharpeners were still saved from general publicity, and the hostile parents, with the help of Miss Toms, drove all the reporters away from the children. The lady reporter settled for trying to make Mr Portland-Smythe say that the visit should never have taken place. When the party had moved off, she looked through her notes and stopped at two words which stood out on their own – 'Brain Sharpeners'. She had a strange feeling that she had been on the edge of a sensational story; but with a shake of the head she tore out the page and screwed it up.

Time passes quickly, and it seemed that no sooner were the children of Class 8 back in England than they were in school again, and Mr Browser was busily marking books as if they'd never been away.

'It's far too hot for work,' whispered Spiky. 'Can't we start old Browser off on some yarn?'

Michael needed no encouragement.

'Please, Mr Browser, the sun is shining in my eyes. May we have the blinds down?'

'You may,' said Mr Browser, smiling. 'Though I would hardly have thought you'd be upset by a little English sunshine, after your experiences out East.'

'Please sir,' called out a boy who had missed the trip, 'was it as hot out there this time as when you were there before?'

'Hotter,' said Mr Browser – and a number of the class put down their pens and waited hopefully. 'But if you want to find out how hot it was,' went on Mr Browser, 'you only have to ask your friends who have been there. But ask them after school. We have too much work to do now, so kindly all of you continue with it.'

More than one face showed disappointment. It had been a great adventure out East, but alas, it seemed to have killed off all those stories that Mr Browser loved to tell in the past. Michael stared sadly at Mr Browser.

'Hurry up, Michael,' Mr Browser urged him. 'By now you should know it's wisest to do what you're told. Maybe I'll take you on another trip one day – but not so far!'

He stood up and walked round the classroom to make sure that everyone was working, and thought to himself that he would never go any farther with Class 8 than, say, the Tower of London. Even on a visit like that there could be excitement enough with Spiky and Michael and Anna around.

Only once did the Brain Sharpeners surface in the minds of Spiky and Michael, when they talked together in a corner of the playground behind a concrete block.

'They won't come back again, do you suppose?' asked Michael, and Spiky shook his head.

'You heard what Mr Salt was talking about after they'd gone. I think they found us too stupid and the tribesmen too dangerous. They won't want us to develop their other planets.'

'Thank goodness for that!'

'There's only one thing,' went on Spiky. 'They might be so mad that they've failed, that they may think of taking over down here on earth, especially if we send rockets out into space. They won't want us to become too clever.'

'Too much trouble,' said Michael.

'Yes, but if something happened to their own planet – they might just have us on their list.'

'I hope not,' said Michael. 'I don't want my brain sharpened or deadened. I like it just the way it is.'

Anna's head appeared over the top of the block.

'I heard you,' she said, 'talking about your brains. No wonder you didn't have much to say!'

Then she jumped away from the block and ran like a hare – with Michael and Spiky after her. Chivvy Chase School was very much back to normal. There were some changes after the visit. Mr Portland-Smythe retired from the Parents' Association and lived happily with his wife, who now found little to worry about after her experiences out East. Miss Toms was the same; sometimes she saw children looking at her handbag, and wondered why. They were, of course, wondering if she still carried her pistol in it.

As for poor Mr Salt, on whom the Brain Sharpeners had taken their revenge, his brain never recovered its former glory. This time he had to retire for good, and the school was taken over by Mr B. Sage, who was never quite sure what was going to happen next at Chivvy Chase.

More Beaver Books

On the following pages you will find some other exciting Beaver Books to look out for in your local bookshop

BEAVER BESTSELLERS

If you enjoyed this book, why not read some more of our bestselling Beaver books. You'll find thrilling stories, hilarious jokes and crazy poems for everyone to enjoy. They are available in bookshops or they can be ordered directly from us. Just complete the form below and send the right amount of money and the books will be sent to you at home.

☐ THE FOLK OF THE FARAWAY TREE	Enid Blyton	£1.75
☐ NICHOLAS AT LARGE	Goscinny and Sempé	95p
☐ EMIL AND HIS CLEVER PIG	Astrid Lindgren	95p
☐ REBECCA'S WORLD	Terry Nation	£1.50
☐ CONRAD	Christine Nostlinger	£1.50
☐ LITTLE OLD MRS PEPPERPOT	Alf Proysen	£1.25
☐ THE MIDNIGHT KITTENS	Dodie Smith	95p
☐ THE GREAT ICE-CREAM CRIME	Hazel Townson	£1.25
☐ BOGWOPPIT	Ursula Moray Williams	£1.75
☐ THE SIEGE OF WHITE DEER PARK	Colin Dann	£1.75
☐ THE WINTER VISITOR	Joan Lingard	£1.25
☐ SNOWY RIVER BRUMBY	Elyne Mitchell	£1.25
☐ BEOWULF	Robert Nye	£1.25
☐ GHOSTLY AND GHASTLY	Barbara Ireson (editor)	£1.50
☐ HOW TO HANDLE GROWN-UPS	Jim and Duncan Eldridge	£1.25
☐ HOW TO SURVIVE SCHOOL	Don Shiach	£1.50
☐ IT'S FUNNY WHEN YOU LOOK AT IT	Colin West	£1.25
☐ MAGIC TOYS, TRICKS AND ILLUSIONS	Eric Kenneway	£1.50
☐ MY FAVOURITE ANIMAL STORIES	Gerald Durrell	£1.95

If you would like to order books, please send this form, and the money due to:

ARROW BOOKS, BOOKSERVICE BY POST, PO BOX 29, DOUGLAS, ISLE OF MAN, BRITISH ISLES. Please enclose a cheque or postal order made out to Arrow Books Ltd for the amount due including 30p per book for postage and packing both for orders within the UK and for overseas orders.

NAME ....

ADDRESS ....

....

Please print clearly.

BEAVER TITLES FOR YOUNGER READERS

If you're an eager Beaver reader, perhaps you ought to try some more of our exciting titles. They are available in bookshops or they can be ordered directly from us. Just complete the form below and enclose the right amount of money and the books will be sent to you at home.

☐	MR BROWSER AND THE MINI-METEORITES	Philip Curtis	£1.50
☐	THE GREAT ICE-CREAM CRIME	Hazel Townson	£1.25
☐	MIDNIGHT ADVENTURE	Raymond Briggs	£1.25
☐	NICHOLAS AT LARGE	Goscinny and Sempé	95p
☐	EMIL GETS INTO MISCHIEF	Astrid Lindgren	£1.25
☐	BOGWOPPIT	Ursula Moray Williams	£1.75
☐	THE FOLK OF THE FARAWAY TREE	Enid Blyton	£1.75

If you would like to order books, please send this form, and the money due to:

ARROW BOOKS, BOOKSERVICE BY POST, PO BOX 29, DOUGLAS, ISLE OF MAN, BRITISH ISLES.

Please enclose a cheque or postal order made out to Arrow Books Ltd for the amount due including 30p per book for postage and packing both for orders within the UK and for overseas orders.

NAME ....

ADDRESS ....

....

PLEASE PRINT CLEARLY